Robot Riots

THE GOOD GUIDE TO BAD BOTS

Alison Bing
and Erin Conley

BARNES
&NOBLE
BOOKS
NEW YORK

ISBN 0-7607-3000-8

Text design by Lunquist Design, New York

Printed and bound in the United States of America

02 03 MP 9 8 7 6 5 4 3 2 1

RRD-H

... for all the people whose dreams are populated with robots (you know who you are)

Special thanks to Marco and Graeme, our robot widowers; Carlo Bertocchini, our technical advisor and a true champion of the sport; Marc Thorpe, chief robot instigator and visionary; Greg Munson and Trey Roski, superheroes of the robot world; Jim Smentowski, goodwill ambassador extraordinaire; Rick Campbell and Heather Russell-Revesz at Barnes & Noble, who are the reason you're reading this; and the good people at BattleBots®, Inc., The Learning Channel®, and Mentorn Barraclough Carey Ltd., who show us the fun side of science.

Our heartfelt appreciation goes out to all the people that have made this book and robot sports such a distinct pleasure, especially: Jason Bardis; Michael Bastoni; Gillie and Vincent Blood; Reason Bradley; Dion Brewington; Alex Burke; Christian Carlberg; Emma Cathcart; Gage Cauchois; Dan Danick; Nola Garcia; Donald Hutson; Grant Imahara; Mark Joerger; Roger Korus; Andrew Lindsey; Fiona Mason; Chuck McManis; Bob Pitzer; Ilya Polyakov; Dr. Joanne Pransky; Pete Redmond; Jonathan Ridder; Mark Setrakian; Tony Somerfield; Jenny and Ian Smith; Dave Thau and Kirsten Menger-Anderson; Mike, Beck, Lisa, and Rik Winter.

Alison would like to give endless thanks to the Bing family and Erin would like to extend big thanks to the Bernhard and Conley clans. Thanks also to the super staff of Into Video, People's Café, and Amazing Fantasy Comics—look 'em up when you're in San Francisco.

chapter 1

BAD ATTITUDES AND
brainiacs:

The Dirty Lowdown on the Bot Scene

Don't look now: Robots are taking over the world

But it's not like we humans imagined it would be…it's way more fun. There's no bloodshed, no hostile takeover, no humans turned into drones. Robots haven't had to fight humankind to take over; they've won us over by fighting each other. Pit two robots against one another, and we're positively riveted. Robots don't rule over us—they just *rule*.

Skeptical? Just look around, already. Odds are there's a bot match coming soon to an arena near you. And you can always catch one on TV— they're on at least three channels these days. Battlebots®, Robotica®, Robot Wars®—you've got

Robot Wars® house robots preside over the arena
Photo courtesy Mentorn Barraclough Carey Ltd.

your pick of robot combat competitions. Watch, and learn.

Robot mania: The symptoms

Before the action even starts, you'll notice that some fans have the name of their favorite robot scrawled across their torsos in Magic Marker. Homemade signs abound—and woe betide those seated between the bearers of the sign that says "Wedges kick bot!" and the one that says "Wedges are for wimps!" Stats are recited, strategic strengths and weaknesses compared; bot buffs aren't afraid to own up to their obsession. "I'm spending my kids' inheritance on robots!" announces one bot builder's sign.

Then the action begins. The fans jump to their feet, press up against the bulletproof safety barrier, and cheer each time metal hits metal. When sparks fly, the crowd roars. When the action slows down, the crowd chants to egg on the competitors. Tournaments can be long—Robot Wars®, Battlebots® and Robotica® all run four or five very long days— but some fans pack lunches so they don't miss a single crucial minutes-long battle (just be glad no one's thought of bringing a chamber pot...yet). At the end of the day, fans are rubbing their strained eyes and numbed behinds—odds are, they haven't strayed far from the battleground for the past eight hours. They trickle reluctantly out of the arena, lingering near the pits in the hopes of talking with one of their bot-builder heroes. Bot matches blur the line between fan and fanatic.

It is absurd to say that the age of miracles is past. It has not yet begun. - Oscar Wilde

What's come over these people? Ask, and they'll probably say it has something to do with adrenaline, destruction, and ingenuity. Bot combat combines all these elements, and more—it's an art, science, and sport all rolled into one. Robot mania is a wild ride that's hard to explain; you just have to be there. Yes it's a riot, but it's by no means a *regular* riot. You can call it divine inspiration or you can call it temporary insanity—but there's no denying that in the arena, the robots call the shots.

Where did it all begin?
A brief history
of robot mania

Nothing can prepare you for the future shock of your first robot competition. Robots have been dangled out in front of us as the ultimate, tantalizing carrot to our technological progress for so long now that it's hard to believe they're really here, and they're ours for the fighting.

Maria from *Metropolis* (Everett Colletion)

The mere thought of five to six hundred robots fighting for our affections in an arena may make you scratch your head in wonderment—but the fact of the matter is, we live in head-scratching times. Not long ago we were puzzling over how a highway could be paved with information; today e-mail is a term understood even by those who reside under rocks. Besides, we had fair warning: science fiction has been predicting the imminent arrival of scores of robots as far back as the 1920s, when Karl Capek's 1920 play *R.U.R.* first coined the term "Robot." Now science has finally caught up with its fiction, and trumped it.

Way back when

Designation	**Maria, The Robot**
Source	*Metropolis* (1927); also weird 1981 version with color filters and painful '80s pop music
Looks like ...	Feminine version of the Chrysler Building
Famous for ...	Fritz Lang's brooding but brilliant vision, the gold standard for sci-fi. Note to collectors: Hang on to those movie posters—they're also worth their weight in gold.

Twiki (Everett Collection)

Designation	**Twiki**
Source	*Buck Rogers in the 25th Century* comic (1929–1967); radio serial (1932); film short (1934); TV show from 1950–51, revived for two seasons in 1979–81, launched with feature film in 1979
Looks like ...	Anthropomorphic vacuum cleaner
Famous for ...	First film drew crowds at the 1935 World's Fair in Chicago and (like the radio show) moved mountains of tie-in merchandise. Undistinguished '50s TV show briefly resurrected in late '70s using gadgets leftover from *Battlestar Galactica*.

The '50s and '60s:
Our robotic pals

Our obsession with technology probably dates back to the invention of the wheel, but most pop culture mavens would trace the origins of today's robot mania back to the 1950s, when techno-futurism seized the popular imagination. Soon, people predicted, robots would do our chores for us and give us more leisure time. Just like in *The Jetsons*, robots would dress us, feed us, brush our teeth, and send us on our merry way to invent fun new gadgets. Isaac Asimov's "Three Laws of Robotics" assured skeptics that robots would always keep humanity's best interests in mind. If bad robots were to come along, we could always use our handy-dandy remote-controlled robots like Gigantor and the Sentinels to fight them off. But most robots that seemed menacing at first weren't so bad once you got to know them. Take for example Robby in *Forbidden Planet*, or Gort in *The Day the Earth Stood Still*; they looked weird, but they meant well. The cardinal rule of life in postwar subdivisions extended to robots too: As long as we were neighborly, we'd all get along just fine.

1950s/60s

Designation	**Gort**
Source	*The Day the Earth Stood Still* (1951)
Looks like ...	Jiffy Pop® in a helmet
Famous for ...	This bot is so misunderstood and maligned by belligerent humans, it's no wonder he wanted to blow us all up. A daring, insightful metaphor for Cold War brinksmanship.

Gort (©Bettmann/CORBIS)

Designation	**Robby the Robot**
Source	*Forbidden Planet* (1956); recycled in 1957 feature film *The Invisible Boy*; look also for Robby's cameos in *Lost in Space*, *The Twilight Zone*, *The Addams Family*, *The Love Boat*, *Mork & Mindy*, and *Clueless*

Robby the Robot (©Bettmann/CORBIS)

Looks like ...	the Michelin Man®'s daddy
Famous for ...	Robby became the undisputed star of first multi-million-dollar science fiction movie, thanks to MGM art director Robert Kinoshita's distinctive design.

Designation	**Kronos**
Source	*Kronos* (1957)
Looks like ...	LEGO® with legs
Famous for ...	This robot is hell-bent on stealing all Earth's energy, so naturally he heads for California—presumably to take a meeting with PG&E. A cult classic.

Designation	**Gigantor (a.k.a. Tetsujin 28-go)**
Source	*Gigantor* Japanese comic (1958–1966) and animated TV series (1963–1966); comic revived in 2001
Looks like ...	Remote-controlled steel snowman, complete with carrot nose
Famous for ...	Walloped other giant robots that resembled abominable snowmen, and fueled Japanese anime craze in U.S.

Rosie the Robot (Everett Collection)

Designation	**Rosie the Robot and assorted others**
Source	*The Jetsons* animated TV series (1962–63), plus *The Jetsons Meet the Flintstones* TV special in 1987 and animated feature film, *The Jetsons*, in 1990
Looks like ...	Funky cocktail shaker on wheels, wearing a French maid's outfit
Famous for ...	Vintage Hanna-Barbera, with an impact far beyond the 24 episodes that were produced. Predictable jokes and tired *Honeymooners* plots abound, but Rosie and other fantastic gadgets and futuristic settings redeem all.

Designation	**The Vision (a.k.a. Victor Shade)**
Source	*The Avengers* comic (1963); also appeared in *Captain America* and other comic series
Looks like ...	Badass in a bejeweled bathing cap
Famous for ...	With golden eyes, red face, and gold and green gear, he's a truly Marvel-ous vision. Betrayed evil creator Ultron to serve heroic Avengers as shield, computer expert, battering ram and eye candy.

Designation	**Astroboy (a.k.a. Tetsuwan Atom)**
Source	*Astroboy* 1963 animated TV series and comic
Looks like ...	Mickey Mouse/Elvis in hot pants and Paddington Bear boots
Famous for ...	Surprisingly compelling plot lines—our boy hero even has to fight own brother, Atlas. Creator Osamu Tezuka is widely credited as the master of Japanese *manga* style comics.

Designation	**The Daleks**
Source	*Dr. Who* TV series, 1963–1989, and 1965 feature film, *Dr. Who and the Daleks*
Looks like ...	Jell-o® filled lighthouses in samurai armor
Famous for ...	The BBC's enduring contribution to sci-fi with a whopping 695 episodes. The Daleks were the evil bane of Dr. Who's existence, buzzing around his head as he attempts to escape in a busted police box time machine.

Designation	**The Sentinels**
Source	Appearances in *X Men* comics (1964–65), Fantastic Four tribute (2001) and others
Looks like ...	Mighty, menacing Mayan statues
Famous for ...	Stan Lee and Jack Kirby work their magic. These behemoth bots aren't really bad; they're just programmed to mutilate mean mutants.

Designation	**The Robot**
Source	*Lost in Space* TV show (1965–68); re-made as kitschy 1998 film
Looks like ...	Coffee percolator on steroids
Famous for ...	Responsible for arguably the most over-quoted line in science fiction. Bouffants made the female co-stars almost as tall as the towering Robot.

The Robot from *Lost in Space*
(© Bettman/Corbis)

The '70s and '80s:
Those sinister cyborgs

So what happened to our visions of robot-assisted recreation? Well, robots really did come along to take care of our chores for us—and left a lot of unemployed autoworkers with more leisure time than they needed. Our cute cartoon robot sidekicks were replaced by dangerous *Blade Runner* cyberpunks out to get us. It seemed like only a matter of time until all of our creations turned on us, as they did in *Westworld*, *The Stepford Wives,* and *The Terminator*. Disco-ers gave robots an even worse name with a jerky dance called The Robot, arguably the least smooth move ever. Sure, technology wasn't always evil—but it wasn't that much fun either. We wound up with ATMs on every corner, but no robot butlers like Woody Allen's *Sleeper* promised. R2D2 and Hewey and Dewey from *Silent Runnings* were harbingers of virtual pets to come—but what with wars raging hot, cold and on drugs, people were usually too preoccupied with the present to cozy up to the future.

1970s/80s

Designation	**Huey, Dewey, and Louie**
Source	*Silent Runnings* (1971)
Looks like ...	Biped air conditioners carrying flowered watering cans
Famous for ...	Winsome robot environmentalists. (Rumor has it that the bots were played by amputees.) Joan Baez supplies most incongruous sci-fi soundtrack ever.

Designation	**assorted villains**
Source	*THX 1138* (1971)
Looks like ...	Jack-booted, turtleneck-wearing hipsters in masks and bike helmets
Famous for ...	An Orwellian parable involving sex, drugs and Robert Duvall. First film from boy prodigy George Lucas, adapted from a short he made while still in school.

THX villians (Everett Collection)

Designation	nameless
Source	*Sleeper* (1973)
Looks like ...	British butler meets Martian Popping Thing
Famous for ...	Woody Allen (before he went all dark and brooding) gives funniest impersonation of a robot ever—great scene with the Orgasmatron.

Woody Allen as robot
(Everett Collection)

Designation	**Credits read: "Robot Gunslinger"**
Source	*Westworld* (1973); see also the sequel, *Futureworld* (1976)
Looks like ...	The King of Siam (a.k.a. Yul Brenner) minus the offensive make-up, plus black cowboy hat
Famous for ...	Outlandish premise: vacationers in a futuristic, Wild West version of Fantasy Island are stalked by robots run amok. Say what? Great film, though.
Designation	**Carol Van Sant and friends (a.k.a. former members of the Stepford Women's Consciousness-raising Society)**
Source	*The Stepford Wives* (1975)
Looks like ...	High-tech housefraus in frilly maxidresses

Robot Gunslinger
(Everett Collection)

Famous for ...	Spouses at their most sinister. Title now synonymous with both suburban superficiality and poor fashion sense.

C3PO and R2D2 (© Bettmann/Corbis)

Designation	**C3PO and R2D2**
Source	*Star Wars* (1977), see also sequels *The Empire Strikes Back* (1980) and *Return of the Jedi* (1983) and prequel *The Phantom Menace* (1999)
Looks like ...	Brass-plated, patrician android, and his irresistible VW-bug-meets-transistor-radio sidekick
Famous for ...	C3PO plays the scolding straight man, while irreverent R2D2 steals the show with his bleeping and flashing comic stylings. Say what you will about the plot, but Lucas' inventions are sheer genius.

Pris from *Blade Runner* (Everett Collection)

Designation	**Replicants (Pris, Roy Batty and others, mostly villains)**
Source	*Blade Runner*, novel by Philip Dick and 1982 film by same name
Looks like ...	Daryl Hannah, Rutger Hauer, et al working that whole punk gymnast thing
Famous for ...	Daryl does backflips to die for (literally). Worth seeing twice, for studio-released version and Ridley Scott's director's cut.

Designation **Terminator**

Source *The Terminator* (1984) and *Terminator 2: Judgment Day* (1991)

Looks like ... Armored Arnold Schwarzenegger (except for a few morphing moments, that jawline is unmistakable)

Terminator
(Everett Collection)

Famous for ... The effects, of course—is there any other reason to see a James Cameron movie? In *T2*, note T-1000, the liquid mercury version of that guy who plays Doggett on *The X Files* (Robert Patrick).

Designation **Number 5**

Source *Short Circuit* (1986); see also sequel (if you must): *Short Circuit 2* (1987)

Looks like ... Mechanized ET

Famous for ... An '80s classic (if that isn't an oxymoron), featuring *The Breakfast Club* girl (Ally Sheedy), that guy from *Police Academy* (Steve Guttenberg), major hair, weird synthesizer music meant to sound like a computer, and a cuddly robot.

Number 5
(Everett Collection)

Designation **Murphy**

Source *Robocop* (1987); see also sequel *Robocop 2* (1990) and comics; for truly die-hard fans, there's also *Robocop: Prime Directives* TV miniseries (2000)

Looks like ... Extra from *CHiPs* with bulletproof breastplate and a built-in gun in his leg (created by Brian Dewe of Team Deadblow)

Famous for ... Turned evil corporate bots like Ed 290 into scrap metal, and melted that mean Dr. Romano from *E.R.* Fearless Robocop also fought Terminator in a 1992 comic series.

Murphy from *Robocop*
(Everett Collection)

Designation	**Heroic Autobots and Evil Decepticons**
Source	*Transformers* comic (1984), toys, animated TV series, movie
Looks like ...	A ray gun...no, a plane...no wait, a garbage chute
Famous for ...	Market saturation. Movie went straight to video faster than a speeding bullet, but popular toys and comic books are highly collectable.

Transformers (Everett Collection)

The '90s:
Technology gets
warm and fuzzy

The future failed to grip the popular imagination again until the '90s, when it got a grip on the stock market. People started to dream out loud again about how much fun our lives would be in the 21st century, after we all retired at 35 to play with our Tamagotchis® and Furbys® (or maybe other, less demanding pets). The Berlin Wall went down, the market went up, and even the robots seemed optimistic: the Terminator came over to our side, the good Transformers always seemed to whoop the bad ones, and Robocop kept the corporate baddies at bay. Human-cyborg hybridization began to take on a certain appeal—especially after Seven of Nine busted onto *Star Trek* in her Wonderbra®-ed spacesuit. *Lost in Space* was re-made as a blockbuster kitschfest—the techno-savvy '90s audience loved to laugh at that stodgy retro-robot warning "Danger, Will Robinson, danger!" We were flush with warm feelings about cyber-anything, tickled all shades of pink with its prospects. Then the bubble economy burst, and technology took us from tickled pink to pink-slipped, just like that.

1990s/00s

Designation   **Lt. Commander Data**

Source   TV series *Star Trek: The Next Generation* (1987–1994); see also *Star Trek: First Contact* (1996) and *Star Trek: Insurrection* (1998)

Looks like ...   Scrawny Bela Lugosi with white contacts

Famous for ...   Constantly saved Captain Picard et al from their human failings, with enough time left over to take up violin. Data (Brent Spiner) makes star turn in the movies with the expression "Lock and load!" Jonathan Frakes (a.k.a. Commander Riker and director of both films) has the good sense to let Data steal the show.

Data (Paramount/ Everett Collection)

Designation   **Eve**

Source   *Eve of Destruction* (1991)

Looks like ...   Exactly like her creator, who's one of those scientist/ supermodels that populate cult movies like this

Famous for ...   Tagline says it all: "They gave her looks. Brains. Nuclear capabilities. Everything but an off switch." (Take heart: Your VCR has an off switch.)

Designation   **COG**

Source   *Fast, Cheap & Out of Control* (1997)

Looks like ...   What your computer dreams of being when it grows up

Famous for ...   Robotics pioneer Rodney Brooks, Director of MIT's Artificial Intelligence Library, gets the recognition he's long deserved.

COG (Everett Collection)

Designation	**Bender**
Source	*Futurama* animated TV show, 1999–?
Looks like . . .	Homer Simpson encased in metal, with the Seattle Space Needle stuck on his head
Famous for . . .	This debauched bot makes Homer Simpson seem positively highbrow. Comic virtuoso Matt Groenig gives him enough good gags to keep the show afloat.

Designation	**Crow T. Robot, Gypsy and Tom Servo**
Source	*Mystery Science Theater 3000*, TV series, 1990–1999
Looks like . . .	Living proof that stuffed animals do have love affairs with household appliances
Famous for . . .	Delivered running commentaries like those old guys in the balcony on *The Muppet Show*, only they were hipper and even more sarcastic, thanks to the acerbic wit of Joel Hodgson (early Robot Wars® participant).

Crow, Mike, and Tom Servo
(Everett Collection)

Designation	**Furby**
Source	Toy
Looks like . . .	Gremlin with special needs and eyelashes like you wouldn't believe
Famous for . . .	Could learn to say "I know you are, but what am I?" but never learned when to pipe down. Created by Caleb Cheung, another early Robot Wars® participant.

Furby (© Reuters Newmedia, Inc./Corbis)

Designation	**Seven of Nine**
Source	*Star Trek: Voyager*, the TV series (1995–2001)
Looks like ...	Barbie with a bad attitude and implants in her head and hand (among other places)
Famous for ...	An overachiever with ADD if there ever was one. Seven recalibrates shields while coping with the Borgs in her head and her own emerging humanity...all while trying to breathe in her skintight body suit. Able acting by Jeri Ryan makes it more believable than it sounds.

Designation	**Tamagotchi**
Source	Toy/devil's minion
Looks like ...	Ms. Pacman's evil spawn
Famous for ...	Taught millions of children that when the baby is hungry, you just put it to sleep indefinitely.

Designation	**Andrew**
Source	*Bicentennial Man* (1999)
Looks like ...	Tin Man had an affair with C3PO's wife
Famous for ...	Andrew the Android sculpts animals from driftwood while theatergoers drift off to sleep. Whose bright idea was it to cast Robin Williams opposite that kid from the Pepsi® ads?

Designation	**Iron Giant**
Source	*The Iron Giant* (animated film; 1999)
Looks like ...	A mountain of steel with a gladiator helmet for a head
Famous for ...	A gentle giant, a memorable tale, and adept animation— even the most hard-boiled robot combat fans will warm up to this one. The voice of IG belongs to tough guy Vin Diesel (*The Fast and the Furious*).

The future:
Friend or **foe?**

Our high-hopes high-tech future may have blown a fuse, but the real techno-visionaries didn't pack it in. They just took cover in basements and garages, and started working on their own robots. We've played out the cycle of discovery, disillusionment and redemption, and now we're looping back around to discovery. As on *Star Wars* and *Star Trek*, it's prequel time—robot builders are taking us back to the future, to a time when we were in control, technology was exciting, and the future gleamed like stainless steel. The essential logic of robot combat is irrefutable: It's way more fun to pit technology against itself than to wrestle with it mano-a-metal. In robot combat, robots can be both friend and foe—it all depends which one you're rooting for.

The visionary is the only true realist. - Frederico Fellini

Not your typical
mad scientists

Team Díotoír's Pete Redmond preparing for his next Mission Impossible.
Photo courtesy Team Díotoír/ Photo by William Murphy

A few years ago, if you'd asked a crowd of people to name their favorite robot builder, they'd think you were joking. At the time, robotics engineers were not exactly household names. Someone might have mentioned Rodney Brooks, Director of Artificial Intelligence at MIT, who was one of the four people featured in the 1997 documentary *Fast, Cheap & Out of Control.* But that would probably be the end of the conversation. The only robot builders most people knew were the ones in B movies: mad scientists with bristly electrified hair who toiled away alone in secret subterranean laboratories.

All that's changing with robot combat. For one thing, you don't see many robot builders sporting lab coats. Why wear lab rat gear when you've got cool custom-designed outfits, like Team Díotoír and Team Fembot? Besides, many robot-builders aren't scientists, or even engineers. Many are tinkerers by nature, people who are forever fixing up cars or computers—like Ziggo builder Jonathan Ridder. Some got their start as go-cart enthusiasts and video-arcade mavens, as Toro's Reason Bradley and Vlad the Impaler builder Gage Cauchois did. "I know robot builders are always classified as geeks, but I'm not finding that to be true," Gage says. At the very least, you'd expect to find lab whites in the closet of Jason Bardis of Team Inferno, since he's an engineering Ph.D. candidate at UCSB writing a thesis on airplane glue. But instead it's full of gear for car racing, swing dancing, DJing and home repairs. So if you want to spot the robot builders at a party, don't bother looking for lab coats. You'd have much better luck seeking out the people who spent their childhoods systematically destroying their toys (see below).

Future roboteers meet UK super-star, Razer
Photo courtesy Team Razer/ photo by Vincent Blood

10 signs your kid is destined to be robot builder

1) Is utterly incapable of allowing a new toy to remain intact for more than one day

2) Builds obstacles for electric train to overcome "so it doesn't get bored"

3) Flips the light switch off and on repeatedly; when warned that fires start that way, looks skeptical and asks: "How?"

4) Pits battery-operated toys against stuffed animals

5) Is forever running out of LEGO® parts

6) Spends hours on an elaborate construction, only to spend five seconds destroying it—then immediately starts rebuilding

7) Has to be reminded by the science teacher that it's unfair to begin a science fair project six months before the other kids begin theirs

8) Includes cutaway views in the usual house-with-clouds kiddie drawing

9) Tries to jump off the boat in the "It's a Small World Ride" at Disneyland to inspect the animatronics more closely

10) Collects cogs and wheels until they take over one corner of the bedroom and mysteriously begin to take shape

LEGO® MINDSTORM™
Photo courtesy LEGO®

The first mistake of Art is to assume that it's serious.
— Lester Bangs

Sure beats Adrenaline Junkies Anonymous meetings

But what would robot builders be doing at a party anyway? Aren't they supposed to be locked away in some dungeon with their creations? Hardly. Most builders' workshops are in their garages, not in some top-secret location. Don't be surprised to see them practice driving their robots in parking lots and driveways near you (especially if you happen to be in the San Francisco Bay Area, where there's an increasingly urgent need for "Caution: Bot Crossing" signs). But unless it's the month before the competition, you'd be more likely to find Nola Garcia and the rest of Team Loki a few hundred feet underwater scuba-diving, Carlo and Carol Bertocchini a few hundred feet up in the mountains hiking, and builders Christian Carlberg or Ilya Polyakov somewhere between on the slopes with their snowboards. Champion builders know when to step away from their bots and escape to the great outdoors.

Move over, Leonardo

But don't go pigeonholing robot builders as gearheaded extreme sports fans. It's been hundreds of years since Leonardo da Vinci first showed that a painter could invent machines, and many of today's builders are likewise technologically talented and artistically inclined. Robot Wars® creator Marc Thorpe is an artist with an MFA degree in fine arts and a long list of screen credits as a model builder for George Lucas' Industrial Light and Magic. Toro and T-Minus team member Alexander Rose works for the LongNow Foundation, which supports futuristic four-dimensional art projects (the perennially avant-garde Brian Eno is a board member). When Mark Setrakian is not busy developing Academy Award®-winning special effects or working his literally and figuratively stunning robots The Master, Mechadon, and Snake, he's a musician who by his own account makes "a racket that sounds like Fatboy Slim meets Rammstein." Likewise, Lisa Winter rocks out on electric guitar, DJs, and plays violin in the Madison youth symphony orchestra when she's not building Mecha Tentoumushi. Now if that doesn't update your idea of the term Renaissance man, nothing will.

The entertainers

Robot combat at its best is like theater where the props have rushed the stage—so not surprisingly, it tends to attract people with a flair for showmanship rather than reclusive science types. Inertia Labs' Reason Bradley acknowledges as an inspiration Survival Research Laboratories, the performance

Grant Imahara gets in a little R&R2D2
(Photo courtesy Industrial Light & Magic)

group known for spectacles featuring robots and general mayhem. Deadblow creator and ILM model maven Grant Imahara is known in the robot world for his work on R2D2 for *Star Wars Episode 1*, but he's also known locally in San Francisco for writing and acting with the Asian American Theater Company Players. Sumo bot builder Dion Brewington is a published poet who enjoys "songwriting, singing, and playing guitar, in addition to restoring antique muscle cars and driving antique tractors in the occasional parade." It may not be often that the words sumo, poet, tractor and parade arise in the course of a single conversation—but in the context of robot combat spectacle, it seems perfectly natural.

A creator is so completely contemporary that he has the appearance of being ahead of his generation.
— Gertrude Stein

Scientists, no—but mad? Well... maybe a little.

Not all bot-builders are mad scientists, but some are admittedly a bit obsessed. It takes a strong vision and fierce determination to get through the long hours required to build a bot, and to front the amount of money required for parts.

But for the most part, builders manage to maintain perspective. There are some exceptions, of course: The builders of UK Robot Wars® champion Razer were so obsessed with their bot that their wives and girlfriends hardly ever saw them. But soon the members of team Razer can expect to be spending quality time with their loved ones again—on the battlefield.

Jenny Smith and the members of team Robot Widows now have their own bot: Widow's Revenge.

Living well is no longer the best revenge: Introducing Widow's Revenge
(Photo courtesy Team Robot Widows/Photo by E. Cathcart)

Engineering **equality**

Girls just wanna build bots: Yvonne Feliciano, Adriana Bermudez and Judith Martinez sand parts to perfection under the supervision of Bill Garcia.
(Photo Courtesy Starbot/ Photo by Bill Garcia)

Which brings us to yet another misconception: robot builders are by no means all male. Granted, there are more men than women in the sport at this writing, but the number of women involved is growing exponentially with every robot competition. "There are more girls getting into this sport all the time," observes Team Fembot member and teen mentor Nola Garcia. "About half the kids at our Starbot workshop are girls, and the girls are doing the welding, engineering, everything. This is great news for the future of engineering, since right now most engineering schools right now are only about 16% women." Builders welcome the increasingly co-ed competition. "I get a lot of fan mail—mostly from teen-agers, usually boys, asking for building advice," says 14-year-old builder Lisa Winter. "But it's really cool when a girl writes and says, 'Hey, I love your bot. How do I build one?'"

Finding your **inner bot** builder

So if builders aren't all male, or reclusive, or sporty, or geeky, who are they, exactly? Read the bot shots of builders scattered through this book. Tune in to a robot combat competition on TV—better yet, attend a competition in person. Locate a robot club near you, and go. You might find you are a lot like a robot builder—in fact, you might find that you *are* a robot builder. Just don't say we didn't warn you.

Still round the corner there may wait/ A new road or a secret gate. — J.R.R. Tolkien

BOT SHOT

Carlo Bertocchini: Robotbooks.com founder/bot builder

Web site: www.robotbooks.com

Team BioHazard: Carol Bertocchini and David Andres, teammates

Robot credits:
   BioHazard (HW)
   The Beast (Sumo robot)
   Stealth (1995 US FIRST champion)

Home base: Belmont, California

Born: 1961

When push comes to shove

I was always interested in mechanical things. Back in 1993, before Robot Wars® and BattleBots®, I built an autonomous sumo robot. I'd been going to the SF Robotics Society meetings awhile when they decided to sponsor a robot sumo competition based on the official Japanese sumo rules—and I thought that sounded great. The goal of sumo robot combat is just to push your opponent out of the ring, so there were really no weapons. Then I went to Robot Wars® in 1994 and 1995 as a spectator, and that started me thinking about what kind of weapons I could make.

Fighting spirit

One of the first bots BioHazard went up against back in 1996 was La Machine, built and operated by Gage Cauchois, Greg Munson and Trey Roski. BioHazard beat La Machine in the one-on-one competition, but then LaMachine damaged BioHazard in the rumble competition. So I was looking forward to a re-match. But then all these sticky legal issues arose in 1997 that made it near impossible to hold robot competitions—until Trey and Greg stepped up and risked a bunch of money to hold the first BattleBots®. They deserve a lot of credit for that. They took a big risk for the love of the sport, and in the end it's benefited them and robot competitors worldwide.

That's why they call it the pits

In the past, it's been kind of a joke among the competitors that I show up with hardly any tools, plug BioHazard in and walk away. That definitely wasn't the case in Season 3. In the match against Son of Whyachi, BioHazard sustained a lot of damage. I was working on my robot almost constantly with David Andres, and it got hectic for me in the pits. The pits are really not the best place in the world to repair robots. You've got 500 teams alongside you, making noise, grinding things—it's just hard to get stuff done, and sometimes you only get 20 minutes between matches. You eat when you can, and you sleep when you have to. But that's all part of the game—the whole point is to have good battles and good battle damage.

Carlo with BioHazard
(Photo courtesy BattleBots, Inc.®/ Photo by Daniel Longmire)

The robot Zenmaster at work

I used to work as a mechanical designer for Tyco Electronics, so the process of designing a robot was almost exactly like the processes I used at work—when I came home, I'd continue doing the same thing I'd been doing all day. But it feels different when you're working on your own creation and you have a passion for mechanical design. I've also spent a lot of time since 1998 developing a robot resource site, RobotBooks.com—and now between RobotBooks and BioHazard, robots have become a full-time job for me. It's a lot of work, but it's great to be able to focus on something you so enjoy.

BOT SHOT

Marc Thorpe: sculptor/visionary

Robot credits: Organized first Robot Wars® competitions

Home base: Fairfax, CA

Born: 1946

From canvas to the big screen

My mother is an artist, and my father used to hustle our stuff around, so into art when I was in high school. I ended up paying for my car that way. At the time, I really didn't appreciate the difficulty of getting along as an artist. I had one benefactor who would call me up and say, "Could you make me a blue one?" So I'd make a blue one, which would take me an hour or two, and I'd charge $300—in the mid '60s, that was enough to pay for whatever I needed. As soon as I got serious about art and I became a sculptor, all that stopped. In 1979 I started working at [George Lucas'] Industrial Light and Magic in the model shop. The first robot I built was for ILM—it was the spider robot that chased River Phoenix and Ethan Hawke in Joe Dante's *Explorers*.

Inspiration in a vacuum

The idea for Robot Wars® came about when I was pursuing an invention that would make vacuuming fun—a Dustbuster mounted on a radio-controlled tank. It was fun, but it wasn't really viable, so I took the vacuum cleaner off the tank and wondered, what to do with the thing. A plethora of battery-powered tools had just hit the market, so I thought: "I'll mount some power tools on it, and make a dangerous toy that can eat its way through a wall—that would be cool!" Then I thought, "Wait a minute: What if I invite other people to do the same thing and stage an event?" So I started promoting the first Robot Wars® event back in 1993, and in Febuary 1994 *Wired* magazine ran an article on it—and suddenly I got flooded with e-mail. It was kind of like *Field of Dreams*: If you say there's going to be a ball field, players will show up. "Build it, and they will come."

Marc Thorpe with robot bug sculpture by Clayton Bailey
Photo courtesy of Marc Thorpe/ Photo by Sean Casey

Art as a matter of survival

I view Robot Wars® as an art-sport. I don't think most people are that comfortable with art as something that goes beyond traditions such as painting and sculpture, even though they might refer to the art of cooking, or the art of listening—but there's no denying that the new sport ignites imaginations. As an art form the sport has no limits; the robots can do and be anything. The sport has turned out to be a huge opportunity for people who have a creative spirit but never had a forum where it can be seen. If they'd had a passion for stone, they'd have a place in the mainstream of stone sculpture—but there was no place for people whose medium was mechanical and engineering. They have creative impulses too, and Robot Wars® gives them a way to express themselves that's extremely exciting and visceral. You're dealing with primal issues of survival vicariously, without having to pay costs of life and limb. We're all mortal, fragile creatures that are living on the brink, from moment to moment, so to play out these fears and fantasies in a way that doesn't cause anyone harm is very liberating.

BOT SHOT

Trey Roski & Greg Munson: BattleBots® co-founders/bot builders

Web site: www.battlebots.com

Robot credits:
   La Machine (MW/HW)
   Ginsu (SHW)

Home base: Novato, California

Born: Trey Roski: 1965
         Greg Munson: 1966

Et VoiLa Machine

GM: [Team Sinister's] Mark Setrakian got me tickets to see the 1994 Robot Wars® competition in San Francisco. I went down there with my wife, Tine, and checked it out. Then an old friend of mine, Peter Abrahamson [of Ronin fame] called and encouraged me to build my own robot for the next competition. At first I wondered if I could do it—could I really build a fighting robot? But then something clicked, and I had that realization that most bot builders have: "I *can* do it"; building one of these machines is totally possible. At that point, a whole spectrum of robot ideas opened up, and I spent the rest of that night tossing around bot concepts with friends. Before bed, I went downstairs to take out the trash and there was my neighbor, Gage Cauchois [who later built Vlad the Impaler]. I told him about my plans to build a robot and immediately he said, "Let's do it." We brought in Trey and we were off. Soon La Machine was born. It only cost $600. Most who saw the robot laughed at it—they thought it was a hunk of junk—until they saw it compete. We won three trophies that first year. But the best thing was when Mark Setrakian, who is one of the most creative people I know, commended us for building such a simple and devious little item.

Time to shine

TR: There are not enough outlets for intelligence these days. That's what the BattleBox™ is for. To get in there, you have to be smart—

though most builders wouldn't even say that about themselves. Smart people are used to not being recognized. If you're a jock, you get to throw a football in a stadium where everyone will see you and appreciate what you can do. But there was no stadium where people could watch genius in action—until robot combat came along. BattleBots® gives intelligent people a place to stand out, to be who they are at their best.

Greg and Trey with Ginsu
(Photo courtesy BattleBots, Inc.®/ Photo by Daniel Longmire)

Bring it on!

GM: What blows us away is watching the sport grow every year. We've gone from around 60 competitors to over 500 competitors in our first two years, and we expect higher and higher numbers in the years to come. From the core group of builders we've expanded to see family teams, school teams, international teams, women's teams, celebrities — a whole spectrum of people with different expertise and ideas. This has inspired us to include regional events, high-school curricula and competitions in our plans for the future. BattleBots® is a true sport and we want it to be known like "Mom, BattleBots® and Apple Pie."

Skewing the learning curve

TR: What excites me about this sport in general and about our new BattleBots® IQ high school program in particular is the huge potential for learning. At school, kids are asking, "Why do I need to know this algebra stuff?" Robot-building shows them the meaning of all those equations: pi means a circle, a sprocket; you need X number of teeth to get Y amount of torque. Robots teach kids to take advantage of technology, instead of being afraid of it and letting technology take advantage of them. They use their brains to build something that expresses who they are, and we all get to witness the results. I've been to so many sporting events, concerts, you name it, and nothing is quite as rewarding as this. Nothing.

BOT SHOT

Mark Setrakian: bot builder/special effects master

Robot credits:
   The Master (HW) Heavyweight Champion,
      Robot Wars® 1995; Best Design Robot Wars®, 1994–95
   Snake (SHW) Strangest Robot, Robot Wars®, 1997
   Mechadon (SHW) Best Design BattleBots®, 1999;
      Coolest Robot, Best Engineering BattleBots®, 2000
   Snake (SHW) (new version) Coolest Robot,
      Best Engineering BattleBots®, 2001

Home base: Los Angeles, California

Born: 1965

Mark the movie maven

When I was five I saw *King Kong*, and I became completely hooked on
monsters and monster movies. As a kid I imagined that movie creatures
were like real robots, more complex than just puppets or guys in suits. My
other great inspiration was to become an inventor. My heroes were Da
Vinci, Tesla, Jacques Cousteau [inventor of SCUBA] and Ray Harryhausen
[special effects master on the original *Mighty Joe Young, Clash of the Titans*
and other films]. I spent about half of my time sculpting monsters out of
clay, and the rest working on my inventions. Eventually these interests col-
lided and I got a job at ILM where I met Marc Thorpe. My first movie was
Howard the Duck. In '88 I moved to L.A. to work with [Academy Award®-
winning effects master] Rick Baker. Some recent projects include *Men in
Black, Mighty Joe Young, The Grinch*, and currently *Men in Black II*.

Tarred and tethered

I built my first fighting machines back in 1990–91—as an after hours
diversion during especially stressful projects. I took a little cute-looking
Fisher Price® truck and gave it a functioning flamethrower. I would enact
these horrible little plays in the studio parking lot to entertain the crew
while we were on breaks. After one particularly destructive performance
that left the parking lot completely scorched, the boss said, "Please don't
do this anymore. I'm starting to have nightmares."

Havoc is The Master's middle name

I came up with The Master for the first Robot Wars® competition. Back then, the arena didn't really offer the crowd a lot of protection. During the match between The Master and The Beetle the crowd was showered with sparks, fiberglass and concrete dust. During the 1996 rumble, The Master's gas-powered saw ripped off and crawled across arena floor on its own power. Meanwhile, The Master was still crashing around with the broken fuel line, spilling gas all over the arena. Nothing bad happened, but after that they added some rules governing fuel lines so that hopefully wouldn't happen again. The Master never really got a full overhaul, and at the last event it finally melted down in the pits after a match, but it will be back to wreak havoc in the arena again soon.

Mark Setrakian with Mechadon
(Photo courtesy BattleBots, Inc.®/ Photo by Aengus McGiffen)

From tongue depressors to death blossoms

For the first BattleBots® competition in Long Beach, I wanted to build something completely different, a monster machine I would have loved as a kid. At work I make little walking creatures out of servos, hot glue, and tongue depressors as a quick way to try design ideas. Two of these models became conceptual prototypes for Mechadon. Unfortunately I only had four weeks to build it. For the first time in my life I found my self sitting in front of this half-finished robot, not having slept for three days, thinking "I've failed, this thing is not going to work." But it did work. I did an exhibition match against Ronin. That was the first time anyone got a good look at Mechadon in action, including me. I had given Mechadon different movement modes for walking, rolling, and the Death Blossom. I remember throwing the mode switches thinking "O.K., what happens when I do this? Holy crap, look at that!" Still, I'm never completely satisfied with my work. All robot builders aspire to more than we can actually deliver, and that's probably what drives us to keep creating.

BOT SHOT

Gage Cauchois: lighting designer/bot builder

Team Vladmeisters

Robot credits:
Vlad the Impaler (1999 and 2000 BattleBots®
heavyweight champion)
Vladiator (Super heavyweight)
La Machine (with Greg Munson and Trey Roski)

Born: Oakland, California 1951

Bot buff, born and bred

When I was 6 or 7, I built a full-size robot costume out of cardboard boxes painted silver, with antennas made out of coat hangers—robots were these big goofy-looking things back then. I think I was genetically disposed to engineering—my grandfather was an engineer, my great-grandfather invented graphite brushes, and now my nephew is into it too. Plus I've got this natural competitive nature; I was always kind of a jock, and I still Rollerblade and play roller hockey and ice hockey. So robot combat came naturally to me.

Ooh la La Machine

I got into building robots through Greg Munson [BattleBots® co-founder], who lived in the same artists' warehouse as me and worked with me on this lighting fixture for a big hotel. Greg knew I liked build-ing things and flying remote-controlled airplanes, so when Robot Wars® came along he said "Why don't you build a robot with me?" On the inside, La Machine was like a funky old computer. Greg did a lot of the electrical and soldering, and Trey [BattleBots® co-founder] drove the thing—and it performed pretty well.

An Impaler is born

After the first BattleBots® competition was announced, I only had 2 months to develop Vlad the Impaler. I teamed up with Greg Walker—he knew how to use compressed CO_2, did all the welding, and made computer renderings of the design. After that event, it was back to the

Gage with Vlad the Impaler
(Photo courtesy BattleBots, Inc.®/ Photo by Daniel
Longmire)

drawing board. I consider all my robots prototypes under construction.
To date, I've probably spent about 2000 hours on Vlad.

Consider yourselves warned

Right now I'm working on Vlad the Impaler 2, which will combine elements of La Machine and Vlad the Impaler to lift, launch, and impale
opponents. Flipping isn't going to affect me. Spinners like Whyachi,
beware: right side up Vlad 2 will be a fighter, but turn him upside down
and Vlad 2 will have something special in store for you.

Crouching tiger, hidden Impaler

I'm into the spectacle of fighting; I like to use the arena as a bouncing
board and make a lot of noise. My model for battle is the one in
Crouching Tiger, Hidden Dragon, with things flying everywhere and bots
driving up the wall—one where no one ever seems to get hurt, but
there's an intensity of battle that's entertaining.

chapter 2

Thrills, Spills & Skills

Life is either a daring adventure, or nothing. — Helen Keller

Raves and Faves

Veteran roboteers may be courted by the press, wooed by sponsors, and worshipped by fans, but there's no question about who the real stars of robot combat are: the robots. "I admire all the robots," says Team Nightmare legend and goodwill ambassador Jim Smentowski. "Anybody who has the ability to come in with something that works deserves credit." But with the sport growing at warp speed, there's a better, stronger, faster bot debuting each new season. As builder Nola Garcia notes, "There were a lot of upsets in BattleBots®, Season 3.0. It's very humbling when a newbie builder blows away a veteran."

Magnetic bots

Win or lose, there are some bots that everyone just seems to love. People gravitate toward certain robots as though they were emitting some kind of mechanical pheromone or raw robot magnetism (hey, it could happen—who knows what some of these builders are capable of inventing!). But combat robots are new arrivals in the world of mean machines, so there are not yet acknowledged robot classics equivalent to, say, a '57 Chevy or a '65 Mustang. Fans can and do track champion robot stats avidly, but there is no real science yet to picking favorites in robot combat—the robots all seem to evolve too quickly for past behavior to be a solid indicator of future performance. So we asked those who know robots best to share some of their own raves and faves. Turns out that builders are fans, just like the rest of us. Here are some of the robots that seem to rank on every builder's list of bad bots.

There was never a genius without a tincture of madness. — Aristotle

BioHazard:
Wasting the **competition**

Main Builder: Carlo Bertocchini

BioHazard is the type of bot that brings builders to their knees. "I almost cried when I saw Carlo [Bertocchini] come in with it," remarks Robot Wars® founder Marc Thorpe. Expertly machined and sleekly designed, this striking heavyweight features six-wheel drive, a mighty lifting arm, anti-wedge fenders, and an exceptionally low center of gravity at only about 4" tall. "I've spent a long time trying to get under those skirts," confesses Vlad the Impaler's Gage Cauchois.

Up, up and away: BioHazard makes a frisbee out of Blendo
(Photo courtesy BattleBots, Inc.®/ Photo by Garry Gay)

Don't expect to see Carlo panicking in the pits or wearing a welding mask; BioHazard is securely held together by over 700 machine screws.

"BioHazard has been a big inspiration to me as a builder," says Deadblow builder Grant Imahara. "It's so soundly engineered that it's nearly impervious to harm, and it's just incredible to look at, too."

An encounter with Complete Control can be an uplifting experience: Complete Control lifts Subject to Change
(Photo courtesy BattleBots, Inc.®/ Photo by Daniel Longmire)

Complete Control:
Armed and dangerous

Main Builder: Derek Young

Middleweight Complete Control has brought robot combat to new heights—literally. This Canadian kingpin has an electric lifting fork and a pneumatic arm that grips, lifts, and carries opponents to their graves. "I really enjoy Complete Control," enthuses Grant Imahara. "The whole idea of being able to pick up another robot and parade it around the arena is just great. It adds layers of humor and humiliation to combat." Complete Control was carefully constructed of high-quality aluminum using less than 10 nuts on the whole bot. Derek Young's craftsmanship and original design make him a perennial favorite in the pits. "All of Derek's work is really out there," says Team Carnivore's Ilya Polyakov. "His stuff is just really cool."

Mechadon, The Master, and The Snake: Pure, evil, genius!

Main Builder: Mark Setrakian

When Mark Setrakian's quixotic creations roll into the robot combat arena, eyes widen and pop in cartoon fashion. Builders are bowled over—they consistently mention Team Sinister's marvels among their favorite robots. "They're really works of art—they're theater," says Shaft and KMM builder Rik Winter. "Mechadon is a thing of beauty; it's a gorgeous machine." By the look of

Killer asp: Mark Setrakian's The Snake takes out Anubis
(Photo courtesy BattleBots, Inc.®/ Photo by Daniel Longmire)

them, you might imagine they'd be perfectly at home on a pedestal in a museum—but make no mistake, these bots are built for action. The

Mighty mighty Minion
Photo courtesy BattleBots, Inc.®/ Photo by Daniel Longmire

Master is a former heavyweight champ with a spinning steel blade, an actuated lifting arm, and what Mark admits is a "freakish range of mobility." The Snake's jointed movement was equally complex and required something other than a standard joystick. So Mark devised his own unique controller: "It was actually a little snake that fit in my hand," he explains. "When you moved the head of the little snake, the big one reared its head in the arena." Truly mind-boggling—and truly Sinister.

Minion:
"A servile favorite"

Main Builder: Christian Carlberg

Christian Carlberg doesn't call his team Coolrobots for nothing. Just consider super heavyweight Minion. "A quick glance at this bot, and you can understand the amount of time that must have been invested in it," says seasoned builder Dion Brewington. "Everything about that bot screams extreme." And when Christian playfully proposes on his Web site that his robot will beat up your robot, it's no joke. Minion's made mincemeat out of many competitors with its 14" fireman's saw, unbreakable drive train, and "Lexan® tongue of wedge-death" (this is one bot you definitely wouldn't want to kiss!). "Minion is pretty awesome," says Inertia Labs' Reason Bradley. "He took Toro's entire front end off in one blow at the season three BattleBots® in San Francisco. We lost all our fluid—and all our flipping power."

Nightmare: Be afraid.
Be very afraid.

Main Builder: Jim Smentowski

For bot builders, Jim Smentowski's heavy-weight dream is a total nightmare. At 6 1/2' long and approximately 4' tall, it can do some serious damage to the robot psyche. This 210-pound monster has an enormous spinning metal disc that rotates at over 300 miles per hour and two *very* big

Raising the fear factor: Nightmare with little bro Backlash
Courtesy Jim Smentowski/Photo by Jim Smentowski

metal teeth. With drive motors capable of towing a car, it's no wonder that Nightmare took home BattleBots® "Most Aggressive" award back in the first BattleBots® event in 1999. Reason Bradley of Inertia Labs deems Nightmare a "total destruction machine, and a definite crowd favorite." "I always love to see Nightmare blow things across the arena," agrees Team Fembot's Nola Garcia.

Razer: Looking sharp

Main Builder: Ian Smith

One look at Razer and it's easy to see why this bad boy tops fans' and builders' top ten lists in the U.K. "Razer is a fantastic piece of engineering," says Team Díotoír builder Pete Redmond. Razer's beautifully brutal, sculptural aluminum and steel form has 450 holes drilled in it to

Razer's edge
Photo courtesy Team Razer/ photo by Vincent Blood

keep the robot's weight down. The team's handiwork may be functional, but it also has won them the respect of their peers, and more trophies than any other robot in the U.K. at ten and counting. With superb self-righting wings and a nine-ton hydraulic crushing arm with a spiked stainless steel tip, captain Ian Smith's creation is a distinguished competitor. "Razer is one of my favorites," says Deadblow's Grant Imahara. "It's got both form and function going for it."

Son of Whyachi: The proof is in the power

Main Builder: Terry Ewert

Son of Whyachi may be the new kid on the block, but he's already left his mark. In a surprising upset, he took a chunk out of reigning heavyweight champ BioHazard, proclaimed victory and took home the treasured Golden Nut at the BattleBots® season 3.0 competition. "Son of Whyachi really

Heavyweight contender: Son of Whyachi
Photo courtesy BattleBots, Inc.®/ Photo by Daniel Longmire

raised the bar on the level of damage to expect in a heavyweight match," says Team Strange BRU's Chuck McManis. Equipped with a crippling three-arm rotor, this 315lb piece of heavy metal came at the competition like a bot out of hell. Team Whyachi exercised serious brainpower to achieve their unique walking robot, capable of marching across the arena at up to 3' per second. "Son of Whyachi is an engineering masterpiece," notes Jason Bardis of the Infernolab.

Toro: Flipping over the competition

Main Builder: Reason Bradley

Whenever this bullish bot is in the BattleBox™ you'll hear the battle cry: "Tor-o! Tor-o!"

Toro's got his very own fan club: the Toro Guys, who strip off their shirts and scrawl T-O-R-O across their bare chests. Weighing in at a whopping 322.5 pounds, Reason Bradley's big baby packs a serious punch with its CO_2 powered flipper. "I love Toro," says builder Chuck

McManis. "That 'pop!' when its arm goes up is just really neat." Team Nightmare's Jim Smentowski is also a fan. "Toro is one of my favorites robots," he says. "It has such amazing thrusting power. It can launch the competition several feet in the air in one instantaneous movement. I need a build-up of 300 miles an hour to do the same thing." Jason Bardis of the Infernolab concurs: "Toro reveals the frightening potential of pneumatics."

Toro: locking horns with the competition—Toro v. Atomic Wedgie
Photo courtesy BattleBots, Inc.®/ Photo by Daniel Longmire

Tazbot: The devil's in the details

Main Builder: Donald Hutson

Heavyweight favorite Tazbot has been taking his toll on the competition since his debut at the 1996 San Francisco Robot Wars®. Built by Donald Hutson and his Mutant Robots team, Tazbot comes equipped with a caveman-style pick ax, a 360° rotating turret, and an interchangeable tail. Hutson caches a wide variety of custom weapons in his toolbox of tricks and hand picks the ultimate weapon for each opponent. "Tazbot is a creative, effective design," notes Team Sinister's Mark Setrakian. "It is a unique character that's never been imitated." The team's Web site boasts that Tazbot's sole purpose is "to destroy and/or immobilize all other fighting robots," but this strange mechanical gladiator is also just impressive to behold. "Tazbot is an awesome looking robot," says Nightmare's Jim Smentowski. "It epitomizes the look and feel of a combat robot."

Vlad the Impaler: Robot royalty

Main Builder: Gage Cauchois

Like his namesake, 14th century Romanian prince and Dracula inspiration, heavyweight champ Vlad the Impaler is a legendary foe. Vlad is a fast, heavily armored bot with a killer front-end steel forklift perfect for prostrating the competition. "Vlad uses some very powerful electric motors," explains Carlo Bertocchini of BioHazard fame. "You can actually hear the tires squealing as he accelerates and turns." But speed and weaponry aren't the only thing Vlad has in

A mean underbite: Vlad taking out Tazbot
Photo courtesy BattleBots, Inc.®/ Photo by Daniel Longmire

his corner of the arena. As veteran sumo robot builder Dion Brewington notes, "Vlad has a solid design and rarely malfunctions. Its powerful drive motors push opponents across the arena and into the spike strip edges with ease. I believe Gage Cauchois is one of the best BattleBots® drivers out there."

Ziggo:
Me-OW!

Main Builder: Jonathan Ridder

Named after builder Jonathan Ridder's notoriously vicious (but beloved) dead cat, Ziggo definitely lives up to his feral legacy. "Ziggo basically ate the last version of my robot KMM alive," says builder Rik Winter. "We could tell things would change when Jonathan showed up with that design." This spinning lightweight features multiple Ni-Cad batteries, a gyroscope to enhance steering capabilities, and steel blades that rotate at 160 miles per hour. Though he tips the scales at just 55lbs, Ziggo has had no trouble clawing his way to the top of his class and has left plenty of scrap metal in his wake. "Ziggo scares me," admits builder Jason Bardis. "He's shredded three of my bots over the last three years."

One ferocious feline
Photo courtesy Jonathan Ridder

Other robots that consistently pop up **on builders' lists** of raves and faves:

Blendo (HW) – Main builder: Jamie Hyneman
"Blendo was one of the first robots that was both threatening and competitive. Jaime did some damage with that thing, and no one wanted to go up against him." — Mark Setrakian, Team Sinister

Chaos 2 (HW) – Main builders: George Francis and Ian Swann
"Chaos is one of my favorites. It's efficient, powerful and well designed."
— Pete Redmond, Team Díotoír

Hypno-Disc circles its prey
Photo courtesy Mentorn Barraclough Carey Ltd.

Competitors beware: here comes Juggerbot
Photo courtesy The Learning Channel

Deadblow (MW) – Main builder: Grant Imahara

"Deadblow really works well. He's unbelievably fast with that hammer, and tuned to the point that he's great to watch in action."

— Mark Setrakian, Team Sinister

Hypno-Disc (HW) – Main builder: Dave Rose

"Hypno-Disc's rotating disc is capable of dishing out serious damage."

— Jenny Smith, Team Robot Widows

JuggerBot – Main builders: Mike Morrow, Chris Gattman, Tom Vaeretti, Ron Ender

"Team JuggerBot's robots are always well prepared and thoroughly tested. Their teamwork in the pits is a model for other competitors to learn from and follow. At Robot Wars® they showed up with a robot built to burst into flames, and dressed in furry cave-man outfits. You have to like that!" — Mark Joerger, Team Run Amok

Mauler (HW) – Main builder: Charles Tilford

"Mauler is a total kick-ass machine." — Greg Munson, BattleBots® co-founder

Octobot (autonomous robot) – Main builder: Jeff Loitz

"I'm very impressed with Octobot's well thought-out design. After pushing the entire sumo ring across the floor, the audience picked it as a favorite as well." — Dion Brewington, Project X builder

Ronin (SHW) – Main builder: Peter Abrahamson

"Peter Abrahamson's Ronin is unique in the BattleBots® world. It has a very strange suspension with tracks that give it a uniquely ominous appeal." — Mark Setrakian, Team Sinister

Scorpion (MW) – Main builder: Shane Washburn
"The Scorpion is an incredible robot, with that lethal tail of his."
— Mark Setrakian, Team Sinister

Squeegee (autonomous robot) – Main builder: Bill Harrison
"Bill's robot Squeegee especially originally intrigued me when it won first at the 1999 Western Canada Robot Games. It was designed with functionality and aesthetics in mind—something not always seen in robot sumo."
— Roger Korus, builder of autonomous sumo bot Chomp!

The Judge (SHW) – Jascha Little
"Like Toro, The Judge reveals the frightening potential power of pneumatics."
—Jason Bardis, the Infernolab

Every act of construction is an
act of destruction.
— Pablo Picasso

Combat **Rocks**

We all get a little protective about our favorite robots. When you think of all the painstaking craftsmanship that goes into these amazing machines, it can make you cringe to see them catapulted into harm's way. Sometimes people will say, 'Oh what a waste—it was so beautiful!' says Robot Wars® creator Marc

Díotoír can take the heat
Photo courtesy Team Díotoír

Thorpe. "But that's just part of the competition—you get over that. None of the competitors are ever overly protective that way. They are in this for the thrills and the excitement." But you can't have excitement without real risk. As Marc points out, watching beautiful things go out in a blaze of glory can be exhilarating, and with robots in an arena that protects the audience there's no danger that someone will get hurt in the process. "You have to realize that when you watch feature films, the new BMW that crashes really crashes. It's in the budget: a $50,000 car wrecked to make that shot. In auto racing, those engines cost a ton of money, and they have a few of them on hand that they burn through when they're competing. Or just think of the wear and tear on athletes' bodies when they run marathons. The risk is substantial with robots, because of the time and expense that's gone into them—but with all the safety precautions in place, there's no threat to anyone's life and limb."

Ever wanted to kill your computer?

Destroying a mass-produced BMW is one thing, and destroying a one-of-kind, sophisticated piece of technology is quite another—the fun factor is that much higher. There's something undeniably thrilling about reducing expensive technology to a heap of worthless, useless rubble. "People like to see the destruction of technically advanced objects," observes sumo bot builder Dion Brewington. We all know first-hand how technology can mis-

Revision Z has a run-in with Ronin
Photo courtesy BattleBots, Inc.®

behave; this is our chance to see it misbehave from a comfortable distance. "Today, I think many people fear technology," says Mark Joerger of Team Run Amok. "They may find it comforting to watch technology being put to the test and showing its weaknesses." For anyone who has ever spent panic-stricken moments in front of a computer screen that has suddenly and mysteriously gone blank, or had a flight delayed for hours due to some technical glitch, robot combat is payback time.

Cheaper than therapy

Couldn't the time and resources that go into robot battles be spent on more productive pursuits? Perhaps—but we're humans, not robots! Even Einstein needed a break now and then. Some choose robot combat—which doesn't entail plaid pants or special investigations, and is highly therapeutic. "It has to be admitted that life is full of near-combat situations: road rage, noisy neighbor rage, even air rage," observes Bulldog builder Tony Somerville. So we all need to blow off some steam from time to time; better that we blow a robot's gasket than our own. "We're constantly stuck in situations where we're not the ones in control—like not getting your frequent flier miles, or having to wait in line at McDonald's forever—and that can be frustrating," explains builder and BattleBots® co-founder Trey Roski. "Robots give you back control over your destiny; in the arena, your survival is up to you. That's the source of the adrenaline."

Good, clean, fun destruction

The uninitiated may fail to see how robots hell-bent on destruction could be good clean fun. Geez, haven't these people ever read a whodunit, seen an action movie, watched the Superbowl—or gone bowling, for that matter? "Is robot combat destructive? Well yes—but so is hurl-

Sparking imaginations: Nola Garcia building a bot
Photo courtesy Starbot/ Photo by Bill Garcia

ing a ball at a bunch of pins, and no one thinks of bowling as violent," observes bot builder and teen mentor Nola Garcia. "With robots that destructive impulse leads to something constructive. It's impossible to watch a match without thinking about how you would build your own robot, or what you would do differently. If we can use that impulse to get kids into education and engineering, that's great."

What is robot combat?

It's an opportunity to kick butt with your brain.

— Mark Setrakian, Team Sinister

It is a sport, not of muscle but brains. For me it is definitely a creative outlet. I express myself through designing and building these things.

— Ilya Polyakov, Team Carnivore

It's a sport, but also an art—it's a spart!

— Dave Thau, bot builder, engineer, fan

Robot combat is what each team makes it, really—it's futuristic. I think at the turn of this new century, we are looking to be like the Victorians and explore new ideas and pioneer inventions. Robotics, mechanics, science, and art are being blended together everywhere you look. Some robots are works of art.   — Gillie Blood, Team Robot Widows

It's an art, sport, and science. It's a sport, because there are rules and an arena, but it's arty. People are always arguing about what it is.

— Reason Bradley, Inertia Labs

Robot combat is a test of skill and a test of endurance. It speaks to

something that evolved in humans a long time before they began to even write. Robotic combat allows us to rejoice in victory without the pain of knowing someone else may be horribly crippled. "Bloodless Gladiators" describes it well.
— Chuck McManis, Team Strange BRU

Robot Wars® battle shot
Photo courtesy Mentorn Barraclough Carey Ltd.

It's more of a dance contest than a football match. Even if you lose, it has entertainment value. — Gage Cauchois, Team Vladiator

It's essentially rock, paper, scissors. — Jonathan Ridder, Team Ziggo

It sparks the brain—it's a great way to get kids involved in science.
— Nola Garcia, Team Fembot and Team Loki, teen bot builder mentor

It's a thrill sport. It's a battle of a perfectionist's design against multiple threats that are unknown and different each time. For the builders it's a release, after spending hours working on a masterpiece knowing that anything overlooked will be taken advantage of. That's a challenge.
— Dion Brewington, sumo bot builder

It's contagious. — Christian Carlberg, Team Coolrobots

Newton says:
Don't touch that dial

If your spouse/mom/resident remote control freak needs to be convinced of the merits of robot combat, try out this Newtonian argument: According to legend, Sir Isaac Newton discovered gravity when a falling apple spoiled a perfectly good nap. By using our leisure time for leisurely pursuits, we leave ourselves open to inspiration. Some bot builders spend most of their time building better wheelchairs, bomb deactivating devices, or environmental protection robots; who knows what inspiration they'll find next in the heat of robot combat? In that sense, bot battles are pure science in the Newtonian tradition—innovation through casual observation and unexpected inspiration.

Explosively
educational

Ready to rumble: Jason Bardis and Missing Link at Bot Bash
Photo courtesy the Infernolab/ Photo by Lauren Herold

Robot combat is a killer scientific experiment; any weakness can and will be exposed in a fight, so the team is that much more motivated to engineer their robot to perfection. "It's extremely educational—I've learned so much that my three engineering degrees never taught me," confirms Team Inferno's Jason Bardis. "Non-violent alternatives like racing or off-roading or other Olympic-style events would be neat to watch, but building a bot for such events may require it by definition to be so specialized that it can't do anything but that one event, which would be disappointing and resource-consuming." Plus it wouldn't be as exhilarating for us home viewers, or as educational; there's nothing like an explosion to drive an engineering point home.

Simple pleasures are the last refuge of the complex. — Oscar Wilde

Bodacious Battles

Robot combat involves smarts, science, skill, and sportsmanship—but battle is the bottom line. Brace yourself; it can get ugly. In the arena, builders may see their dreams, time, and expenses literally go up in smoke. But when the mass mayhem ends in a pile of

Sparks fly at Robot Wars®
Photo courtesy Mentorn Barraclough Carey Ltd.

metal, there's only one thing left to say: "That was so cool!" For fans and builders alike, robot fighting time is an extraordinary rush. Battles last just a few minutes, but when sparks fly and metal meets metal, it's a moment your memory will bank. Whether you're watching from your La-Z-Boy® or sitting boxside, you can be sure you're in for a good show when robots go at it.

The Master of ceremonies: The Master prevails against Subject to Change
Photo courtesy BattleBots, Inc.®/Photo by Daniel Longmire

One downside to winning is that you're often too busy to catch the carnage. When builders do manage to pull their head out of the pits, they have a unique perspective on the action. They know *exactly* what it takes to make it to match time. But does battle actually look different to those who've been in the arena? Not necessarily. Builders get a charge from all the same stuff the rest of us do—worthy competitors, a good fight, and lots of damage. They may have seen a million sparks before, but the action is still electrifying. We asked a few robot builders to share some of those battles they enjoyed the most—both as spectators and as contenders.

Our brightest blazes of gladness are commonly kindled
by unexpected sparks.
— Samuel Johnson

The Master v. Thor:
Robot Wars®,
San Francisco, 1995

There were some really great fights in the early days of Robot Wars®.
The arena barriers were made of plywood and only about 4' high.
There was this one really great battle between The Master and Thor.
Thor had a gas motor, and when The Master cut through one of its
hydraulic lines the whole room started filling with fumes. There were
about 1,000 people in the stands and they were like, "This is great—
smoke!" But we builders were thinking, "I wonder if this is carcino-
genic?" Then Thor hit The Master's fiber saw and it starts snowing this
hardened material. It was a combination of "This is the coolest!" and
"We're all going to die!"   — Rik Winter, Armored Robotics

In 1995, I came back with a better version of The Master and won the
heavyweight championship in an exciting match against Thor. I was
proud of the work I'd done on The Master, and in fact I was under
unbelievable physical stress due to the threat of physical harm to my
robot—it can be hard to detach emotionally from something you've
built. But I'd say it was one of most fun experiences I've ever had. My
entire family was at the event, and I had two days of spectacular fights
and huge butterflies in my stomach. I later had a re-match against Thor
in the U.K. Robot Wars®. By then I could drive better and knew the
robot's capabilities. Thor wound up disabled and spilling fluid all over
the arena.   — Mark Setrakian, Team Sinister

Tazbot v. The Master:
Robot Wars®,
San Francisco, 1996

Everyone expected The Master (a third year entry and former face-off winner) to easily defeat the strange-looking newcomer Tazbot. As the two robots crashed together, The Master revealed a new ability; it could rear its saw up and smash it down upon an enemy's top armor. Again and again it hit Tazbot, but due to Tazbot's great maneuverability the saw never was able to stay in one spot long enough to cut through Tazbot's armor. Tazbot's driver used his robot's unusual weapon to good effect, deflecting many of The Master's blows by swinging the metal arm from side to side. The two robots fought for several minutes, until The Master suffered a crippling breakdown. As The Master's saw arm lifted, it pinched the wiring leading to the Master's tail; at the same time the kill switch on the saw motor was hit by the tail mechanism and was knocked into the off position. In a flash of shorting wiring and a cloud of blue smoke, both of The Master's weapon systems died. Tazbot advanced on the now helpless Master, cornering it. Tazbot hooked its arm around The Master's now dead saw, holding its adversary pinned. After thirty seconds, the scarred but fully functional Tazbot was declared the winner.

> — Donald Hutson, Team Mutant Robots
> (text by Andrew K. Lindsey, Team Spike)

DooAll v. Kill-O-Amp:
Robot Wars®,
San Francisco, 1997

One of the most memorable battles I've seen was DooAll vs. Kill-O-Amp. Just before the competition, this big article ran on the front page of the *San Francisco Chronicle* that featured DooAll. It was a $55,000 robot that does 45 mph and had tank treads. We were all thinking:

"How is that even possible?!" So there was huge anticipation leading up to the event. DooAll's first battle was against Kill-O-Amp, this huge plywood box with two car batteries in it—mostly scrap. So the green light goes on and they go towards each other and this box goes rocketing across the room and hits DooAll. DooAll's tank tread flies up in the air and the Jaws of Life saw gets blown off and skitters across the arena, and that was it. It was amazing. — Reason Bradley, Inertia Labs

Deadblow v. Pressure Drop:
BattleBots® Season 1.0,
San Francisco, 2000

Hammertime: Deadblow pounds Pressure Drop
Photo courtesy Battle Bots, Inc.®/Photo by Garry Gay

My favorite fight would have to be the one where Deadblow went up against Pressure Drop. I'd fought a tough match against Alien Gladiator where the tip of my hammer was broken off, and I only had three hours to drive 45 minutes to my workshop, mount a new pickaxe on Deadblow, and fight traffic all the way back in time for the match against Pressure Drop. We were still putting all the screws in Deadblow as we entered the arena. Then Pressure Drop fought really hard, and I had to do some pretty fast maneuvers to survive. By the end of the match, my arms were tingling and my hands were numb with adrenaline. — Grant Imahara, Team Deadblow

Heavyweight Rumble:
BattleBots®, Long Beach, 1999

The heavyweight rumble at Long Beach in 1999 is definitely one of the best battles I've seen. It was utterly insane! They had to stop the match at one point because one robot welded himself to the metal floor when a battery wire came loose! It was also cool because the bots refused to stop fighting when time ran out. Who is going to come in and stop a bunch of 170lb robots?!   — Ilya Polyakov, Team Carnivore

Mecha Tentoumushi v. Hard Cheese and house robots:
Robot Wars®, U.K., 1999

In the U.K. Robot Wars®, melee I was up against a lot of bots that outweighed me. They have these house robots that are like 600lbs! There was one competitor called Hard Cheese, which was a big wedge that looks like a slice of cheese with a rat on top. When the fight started, I pulled off the rat and the bot blew a fuse. Then I ended up trapping one of the house robots

Robot Wars® house robots line up to take down the competition
Photo courtesy Mentorn Barraclough Carey Ltd.

under my shell. He was gas powered and needed oxygen to keep his motor going, so I basically smothered him. The other house bot has huge treads and he ran over me (I still have tread marks on my bot). But somehow I got away, and when time ran out, I was the only robot still running!   — Lisa Winter, Robot Action League

Razer v. Chaos2:
Robot Wars®, U.K., 1999

We could hardly have picked a tougher opponent than Chaos 2: the newly crowned series 3 UK champion. We had met in battle at a charity event a month previously, and although we won, George Francis had worked us hard and knew he could flip us. The fight commenced and both machines flew at each other before dodging around in a game of cat and mouse. We very nearly got caught by Chaos 2's powerful flipper, but stayed upright and chased them down. Ian powered Razer in, pushing both robots into the arena's side. Simon then brought the crusher down, puncturing Chaos 2's polycarbonate cover: a gush of carbon dioxide confirmed that we had pierced their pneumatics. Having disabled the flipper, the pressure was off: we took our time making sure there was no coming back for George. We fed Chaos 2 to the house robot Dead Metal's arms—he cut into their flipper as we continued to chomp away on their rear end. We let go and moved round to gain a grip and cause further damage, but Chaos 2 was still mobile and escaped. Would George try and shove us into the House Robots and go out fighting? No, he had decided that enough was enough and he intentionally took a dive into the arena pit! We were delighted with the result—we had finally shown the power of our machine. — Vincent Blood, Team Razer

Ziggo v. Defiant:
BattleBots®, Long Beach, 1999

In the early days of BattleBots®, there was a double elimination match structure. Ziggo and Defiant ended up going head to head twice—once early on in the competition, and once for the finals. Both were amazing fights. Ziggo would hit Defiant and *wham!* Pieces would go flying, but Defiant would come running right back for more. At one point, Defiant's front end had been almost entirely ripped off—he was losing his armor and his wheels were coming off, but he just kept at it. Ziggo took home the championship, but Defiant lived up to his name and put on a great show.

— Jim Smentowski, Team Nightmare

Buddy Lee v. Turbo:
BattleBots®, season 2.0,
Las Vegas, Nevada, 2000

Who are you calling a toy?! Buddy Lee bodyslams Turbo
Photo courtesy BattleBots, Inc.®/ Photo by Daniel Longmire

My favorite battle was the Buddy Lee/Turbo match, where I had to go up against my own teammates on Team Loki. Turbo's driver, Eddie Empuero, is my son's best friend—he's been eating dinner at our house and going on vacations with us for years. And here I was pounding away on his robot. We hit Turbo and his inside chains fell off, but it wasn't called as a knockout, so we just kept hitting him. Those three minutes were longest minutes of my life. I was holding my breath almost the entire time. We'd taken a lot from the guys on our team, so I was hoping we'd win. And it just goes to show that even if you're a veteran robot builder, you have to stay on your toes.

— Nola Garcia, Team Fembot and Team Loki

Turbo is a simple, powerful spinning robot. Buddy Lee is a cute robot, a simple aluminum box made to look like a toy fire truck driven by a cute doll. The two fought for the full three minutes. Turbo tore it up pretty well but we [judges] gave the match to Buddy Lee on points. The audience booed us and everyone wanted to know why we scored it that way. They accused us of giving the win to Buddy Lee solely because it's cute. What wasn't obvious on TV (or to most of the audience) was that Turbo's drive system completely failed during the middle of the fight; the only reason it appeared to be still moving at all was recoil from

61

Buddy Lee ramming its weapon. It was a win for Buddy Lee exactly as spelled out by the rules, yet the decision earned us judges no end of flak after the event.

— Andrew Lindsey, Team Spike builder and former BattleBots, judge

Vlad the Impaler v. BioHazard: BattleBots®, season 2.0, Las Vegas, 2000

Clash of the Titans: BioHazard lifts Vlad the Impaler
Photo courtesy Battle Bots, Inc.®/Photo by Daniel Longmire

The battle that really got me hooked was the heavyweight championship between Vlad the Impaler and BioHazard, which was the first demonstration of Vlad's self-righting pneumatic rod. That thing got caught under an arena hammer. The hammer kept bashing away, but Vlad just sat there until eventually the hammer broke. It was hilarious.

— Dave Thau, bot builder and buff

Vlad versus BioHazard was a terrific match—the advantage went back and forth between them for the full five minutes. When you see these finely tuned champion machines being driven by experts, it becomes incredibly exciting; it's a culmination of engineering and strategic mastery.

— Mark Setrakian, Team Sinister

Razer v. Milly-Ann Bug: Robot Wars®, U.K., Series 4, 2000

Our task was to take out Milly-Ann, and considering the damage she had already taken from her previous fight against Pussycat it was something of a foregone conclusion. What we wanted was to provide some memorable footage, but there was a limiting factor to be taken into account.

The Milly-Ann Bug team are extremely nice people and had asked we try not to damage the expensive internals of their machine. The question was how to win the fight in style without incurring the opposing team a fortune in ruined components. The answer lay in the wheels—as they were only cheap, plastic wheels, we could chew 'em up and spit 'em out—so that is what we did. It was extremely funny to see the helpless Milly-Ann sit there while Razer methodically removed every wheel. The crowd loved it and even the Milly-Ann team was laughing. An easy victory, but not without a few problems in the shape of Milly-Ann's 'hair.' KEVLAR® fibers had been used to create a 'wig' for the Bug and these had insinuated their way into our wheels and axles—it took us a good half hour to clean it all off!　　　　　—Vincent Blood, Team Razer

T-Minus v. Sunshine Lollibot:
BattleBots®, season 3.0, San Francisco, 2001

One memorable battle for us was one this year between T-Minus and Sunshine Lollibot. It was a neat robot because it had so much inertia in its spinning disk that instead of getting flipped by our bot, it went 6" up in the air and came down really hard onto us. This was an amazing robot—I mean, it almost

Where the sun don't shine: T-Minus v. Sunshine Lollibot
Photo courtesy BattleBots, Inc.®/Photo by Daniel Longmire

sawed a wheel off our robot. It was a tough battle. We didn't feel great about beating them, though. The builders were maybe 15, and before the match their mom was sitting right behind us and said, "You're my kids' idol, could you take a picture with them?" So we did, and they were super nice. Then we found out that we had to fight them. We ended up destroying their bot. They got their robot together for the rumble, and were placed right next to us. So I'm telling my teammate Alexander [Rose], "Get away from him, he'll hit someone and you won't have to do it." And he says, "I can't do that." So Alexander just turns and filets him. The kid went 10 seconds. It was pretty brutal. You have no friends in the BattleBox™.

— Reason Bradley, Inertia-Labs

Vlad the Impaler v. MechaVore: BattleBots®, season 3.0, San Francisco, 2001

Vlad the Impaler lost the championship this year to MechaVore, but it was a worthy fight. The battle went the full three minutes, and it was a close decision. At the end, both robots were pretty near dead, and I didn't have much of a robot left. If I'd won, I think I would have done what a medieval knight would do: proclaim MechaVore the true winner.

— Gage Cauchois, Team Vladiator

Vladiator v. Minion: BattleBots®, season 3.0, San Francisco, 2001

One of my favorite matches was the Super heavyweight final between Vladiator and Minion. Vladiator fought all the way up through the ranks and had all these battle scars, but he'd made it to the finals. Minion, the reigning champ, was totally confident that he'd be taking home the trophy. Sure enough Minion pins Vladiator and Gage [Cauchois'] weapon got stuck in one of the arena hazards. He tried to back up with such force that his wheels started smoking, but he was still incapacitated. The ref started the 10-second countdown: 5, 4, 3, 2…and right before he hit 1, Vladiator freed himself, did a 180, slammed Minion into the other side of the arena, and won the match. It was pure drama.

— Greg Munson, builder and BatttleBots®, co-founder

*The only cats worth anything are the cats
who take chances. - Thelonius Monk*

What makes a robot a robot?
(Jury's still out... so you
be the judge.)

Webster's Dictionary III: "A machine that looks like a human being and has
the capacity to perform human tasks; a person who works mechanically;
an automatic or remote-controlled device. The word robot was invented
by the Czech author Karel Čapek in his play *R.U.R.*, which stands for
'Rossum's Universal Robots.' The play was written in 1920 and was trans-
lated into English a few years later. The word robot quickly gained cur-
rency in English. Čapek derived the word from Czech *robota,* 'forced
labor, drudgery.'"

Robotics International of the Society of Manufacturing Engineers
(RI/SME): "A robot is a reprogrammable, automatically-controlled, multi-
functional mechanism which can be integrated into a system and interact
with its environment by acquiring and processing sensory data to perform various tasks."

The American Heritage Dictionary of the English Language: "A machine or
device that operates automatically or by remote control."

Academic Press Dictionary of Science and Technology: "Any mechanical device
that can be programmed to perform a number of tasks involving manipu-
lation and movement under automatic control. Because of its use in
Science Fiction, the term robot suggests a machine that has a humanlike
appearance or that operates with humanlike capacities; in actuality modern industrial robots have very little physical resemblance to humans."

BOT SHOT

Lisa Winter: teenager/bot prodigy

Robot Action League: Mike Winter and
Becky Winter, teammates

Robot credits:
Dough Boy (FW)
Mecha Tentoumushi (LW)

Home base: Madison, Wisconsin

Born: 1986

It all began in the basement

My dad was in the 1st Robot Wars® competition (San Francisco, 1994) and has been competing ever since. I used to help him out while he built bots in our basement and he showed me how to put them together. After a while I started thinking, "That doesn't look so hard." In 1996, when I was 10, I built my first robot, Dough Boy. I made a chef's hat and these big puffy gloves for Dough Boy to make him look cool. He almost won the 1996 featherweight title, but lost in the finals to Wedge of Doom.

If looks could kill

I think all robots should look cool. Otherwise, the bots are boring and the audience doesn't really get into it. Tentoumushi is cute, but deadly. The body is actually a sandbox that my dad and I spotted at Toys R' US. The cute design is also a disguise. It tricks people into thinking, "Maybe I should be a little nicer to her." But then they see how fierce I am and that I'll capture their robot and grind them up once they're trapped under my big red shell.

A young mind storms

LEGO® MINDSTORMS™ are a big inspiration to me. They're great cause you can build anything you want and you don't need to follow the instructions. I've always loved to build things. I had Barbies as a kid, but I never really knew how to play with them. I also get inspiration

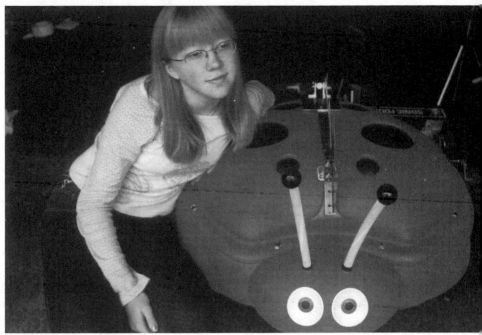

Lisa with Mecha Tentoumushi
Photo courtesy Winter family/ Photo by Becky Winter

from other bots—especially some of the early ones like Mauler, Blendo, my dad's XI, and Mark Setrakian's The Master. I always thought Spiny Norman was really cool. He was a remote controlled car covered with tin foil and nails. He didn't really work, but he was just an awesome bot.

Hot shot, hot bot

Being on *The Tonight Show* was pretty exciting. I had to go to school on the set because I was considered an underage actor. Jay Leno came to my dressing room and talked to me before the show, but I didn't get too much of a big head because we were only there for a day. Going to London to compete in Robot Wars® in 1999 was *really* fun. I was in two fights: one head-to-head and the melee. I won both. It was cool because they have flames and a huge pit in the arena. We wrapped Tentoumushi's interior with aluminum foil and there was a rumor that I did it to cause radio interference, but we were really just trying to protect the bug from the flames.

BOT SHOT

Pete Redmond: avionics engineer/bot builder

Web site: www.diotoir.com

Teammates: Cairon (Zulu) Byrne, Joe Gavin,
    William Murphy, and Johnny Cunnane

Robot credits:
    Nemesis
    Díotóir (Son of Nemesis)
    Díotóir II
    Ulysses
    Nemetóir

Home base: Dublin, Ireland

Born: 1969

Food fight

I've been interested in robots since I was a kid. I remember seeing *Star Wars* and looking at R2D2, thinking to myself, "I could build that, it's just a motorized dustbin." I was only 9. As an adult, I started building weapons like pneumatic dart guns and spud/orange cannons with my [now] teammate, Zulu. We would shoot semi-frozen oranges through steel doors just to see if we could do it. Then Zulu saw Robot Wars® whilst on holiday in America and told me about it. I checked it out on the Internet and found that the BBC was looking for competitors to start up a British version. I immediately applied and we started to build our first robot, Nemesis.

A cuddly killer

When I first built Nemesis, it was just a steel can, but I thought it looked cute driving around on the floor. I decided to cover it with some fake fur and when I saw the red and black spotted pattern in the shop, I knew that was one I wanted. I stuck on a pair of eyes and a big cheesy grin and suddenly it looked like a creature. It gave it character. Everybody laughed at us in the first series because they thought that we had just built robot fodder, but by the end of the competition we had gained a lot of respect.

Pete and Nemesis
Photo courtesy Team Díotoír/ Photo by William Murphy

People realized that just because you're soft and cute on the outside it doesn't necessarily mean you're not hard and dangerous on the inside. Now all my robots have the same face and fur and everybody instantly knows who built them.

Playing with fire

In the UK version of Robot Wars®, there are fire pits and flame-throwers all over the arena. Luckily for me, the judges agreed that fur is cosmetic and does not constitute damage when burned. This means that we have a unique armor. Underneath the furry exterior, my robots are quite fireproof, whereas there are a lot of fiberglass and wooden robots that aren't. We can get our fur burning, move in on another robot, stick some burning fur to it, and set it alight. I usually paste glue all over the fur just before a fight to ensure that it will burn good these days. So I don't try to avoid the flames anymore, I go for them.

Precious medal

I built a robot for Technogames 2001, which is a kind of robot Olympics. My robot, Ulysses, won the gold medal and set a new world record for the internal combustion 25-meter sprint. Ulysses has eight legs and is powered by a 50cc moped engine. Building robots gives me the opportunity to learn more about engineering, and to use my imagination and problem-solving skills. In robot combat, fighting is only a small part of the competition. Designing and building the robots takes a lot more time and effort.

BOT SHOT

Reason Bradley: machinist/bot builder

Team Inertia Labs: Alexander Rose and
   Dave Estrich, teammates

Robot credits:
   Toro (SHW)
   T-Minus (MW)
   Rhino (SHW)
   Lawn Boy

Home base: Sausalito, California

Scrappy from the start

I was born in Sausalito, about 500 feet from my current studio. I had a pretty amazing childhood—there was a huge junkyard nearby, so we could build anything we wanted. My father was a welder, and he had a welding shop across the way—so I knew how to weld by the time I was seven. We'd build 3-wheeled land-sail cars, like a boat you could drive. From the time I was five until I was 16, I got to help build a 36-foot wooden sailboat. There was a pretty good pack of us down here [near the marina], mostly hippie kids. We didn't inter-mingle much with the rich kids on the hill, because when they'd come down they'd hurt themselves.

Art with a bang

My first robot experience was with those wind-up toys you get in Chinatown that make sparks. But in terms of real robots, it would be with Survival Research Laboratories. SRL was my biggest influence. I worked with them for eight months when I was 15, machining stuff that wound up in a show with all this original remote-controlled machinery, 30 cannons, and machines throwing up 80-foot flames. Now that was impressive!

Reason Bradley, Dave Estrich, and Alexander Rose with Toro
Photo courtesy BattleBots, Inc.®/ Photo by Daniel Longmire

There's a Reason for those rules

We heard about Robot Wars® two weeks before it happened, and we barely got our robot done in time. That was Lawn Boy: it had a lawn mower top and engine. The technical guys said it looked OK, but there was no muffler on the engine so it was LOUD—and there were TV interviews going on. They yelled: "Shut it off!" But we couldn't because we'd lost the signal, and no one wanted to get anywhere near the thing. We had to wait 12 minutes for it to run itself down. We got two rules made after us: One was that you have to be able to turn your robot off, and the other was you could only have three minutes of gasoline in your bot. If you can get rules made around you, that's good.

Presto, change-o

So then we had to fix Lawn Boy's antenna before the fight. This guy with long hair and super-long fingernails comes over to us, engineers the thing on his wristwatch calculator from reverse light speed backwards, and says, "Oh, you need to cut off about 12 inches." So we clipped it off, it worked, and we were floored. That's how we met The Master, Mark Setrakian. That's the kind of camaraderie you find at BattleBots®—it's like nothing else I've ever experienced.

BOT SHOT

Grant Imahara: special effects engineer/bot builder

Web site: www.deadblow.net

Team Deadblow: Jon Foreman, Bryan Dewe, Preston Donovan, John Duncan, Nelson Hall, Jamie Hyneman, Scott McNamara, Adam Savage, teammates

Robot credits:
The Energizer Bunny (second generation)
Merrimac (with ILM team)
R2D2 (*Star Wars: Episode 2*)
Deadblow (MW) (BattleBots® Rumble Winner 1999, Long Beach, CA; BattleBots® Season 1.0 Comeback Robot of the Year; BattleBots® Season 1.0 Middleweight Runner Up; BattleBots® Season 2.0 Middleweight Rumble Winner)

Home base: Oakland, California

Born: 1970

Getting hammered

I knew when I attended the 1995 Robot Wars® that I wanted to build a fighting robot of my own. The idea for Deadblow came from Thor, the granddaddy of all hammer robots, who was a lot of fun to watch. He was one animated robot, hammering so hard that it made him hop up and down. Back then, I knew very little about robot combat. Fortunately, I got a two-week job at the Model Shop at Industrial Light and Magic and got to work on the ILM team for the 1996 Robot Wars®. That two-week job turned into a career, and five years later, I'm still there.

Terrier, toaster, toy

Deadblow has a lot of animal-like qualities. The hammer strikes rapidly, so it makes the robot seem excited. It also has the ability to mount another robot, climbing right up onto its opponents and hammering away at them from above. This is why a BattleBots® announcer once

Grant with Deadblow
Photo courtesy Grant Imahara

compared Deadblow to "a terrier in heat." In the very first Battlebots®
competition, someone said that Deadblow looked like a toaster with a
hammer, which traumatized me, since toasters don't usually inspire fear.
So I decided to rebuild Deadblow from the ground up, and make it a lot
sleeker. I modeled the new design in CAD, made a prototype in clear
acrylic, and then machined each part to match the acrylic model. I can't
tell you how many hours I spent obsessing about the aesthetic details,
but now that Deadblow is being made into a toy, I'm glad that I did.

Deadblown away

Being at Battlebots® competitions is amazing—there is such a congenial
atmosphere. It's like a really cool party, and your robot is your ticket to
enter. When I was wheeling Deadblow into the arena for season three of
Battlebots®, I had a blanket over top of the robot so all you could really
see was one wheel and the back of the hammer. A 4-year-old kid ran up
to the robot and yelled "Deadblow!" and pointed up to me and said,
"Grant Imahara!" I was speechless. When I started building Deadblow, I
never thought that I would have fans all over the world, or toys of my
robot. Back then, it was all about bashing robots together for fun.

Star warrior

I remember seeing R2D2 and C3PO as a kid and thinking that maybe
one day I would build robots that cool. I never really thought that I
would be part of a team of effects specialists working on the real
R2D2, but here I am. Preparing R2D2 for a movie shoot is a lot like
preparing a fighting robot for battle—you never know what conditions
your robot will face, so you make him as foolproof and rugged as you
possibly can. In the end, I think that both Deadblow and R2D2 have
done very well for themselves.

BOT SHOT

Jonathan Ridder: network manager/bot builder

Teammates: Douglas Ridder and Linda Ridder

Robot credits:
Ziggo (LW)

Home base: San Jose, California, USA

Before the bot boom

I didn't really get into robots until I saw the first combat robot event, Robot Wars®, in 1994. After that, I was hooked and decided to build my own bot the following year. There were very few resources at the time—news groups, but not much else. I kind of had to cut my own path, which made it hard. I was lucky to drive my first robot at all.

A lightweight legend

Ziggo was conceived in 1997 and is named after my deceased cat, Ziggy ("the meanest cat to ever walk the earth"). His first competition was in a parking lot with seven other robots. He shredded everyone he went up against that day. Ziggo's design was inspired by the heavyweight Blendo, the most destructive robot of his day. I decided to build a light-weight that would do as much damage. I knew I needed slopping sides so that if I stopped spinning and someone rammed into me, the design would act like a wedge and deflect the energy. I went to the wok shop in San Francisco's Chinatown and got a 20" wok for the shell. That was the very first part I got for Ziggo.

Out with a bang

Bot builders aren't as competitive as you might think. It's not at all unusual for people to help out their opponents—people want a good match. No one wants a weak loss. If you're going to go out, you want it to be spectacular. In his very first match, Ziggo knocked a piece of his opponent's saw off and all the way out of the arena. I almost got kicked out of the match, but they let me slow down instead. It's just amazing how helpful and open people are with each other—even with their

Jonathan with Ziggo
Photo courtesy Jonathan Ridder/Photo by Linda Ridder

ideas. There aren't a lot of secrets. Of course, there *are* certain things people want to keep to themselves.

The perfect bot

Bot building hasn't converged to an ideal design yet. It's still a fairly new thing there are no real set tricks of the trade. Robot combat is very visual—it's just neat to watch because of how nicely the bots are built. Each one is crafted individually so there's definitely an artistic element. But people also just like the destructive nature of the sport—there's a real rush involved. The competition has a certain sense of urgency and excitement. Fans like to root for their favorite robots—and to watch hi-tech stuff get destroyed.

chapter 3

Deadly Designs

Art at its most significant is a distant early warning system that can always be relied on to tell the old culture what is beginning to happen.
— Marshall McLuhan

It's bound to happen sooner or later. There you are, watching the bots go at it on TV, when suddenly you're gripped by The Idea: "If that were my robot, I would have designed it so it could…" Your pulse races; you get a surge of adrenaline; you feel a slight tingling sensation in your palms. Don't bother with CPR or the Heimlich Maneuver—get yourself a pen and paper, STAT. There is no other known cure. Once The Idea has you in its clutches, you are stuck with it until you have either realized it, or been seized by The Next Idea. Don't be alarmed. Robot builders are proof positive that it is possible not only to live with The Idea, but to embrace it.

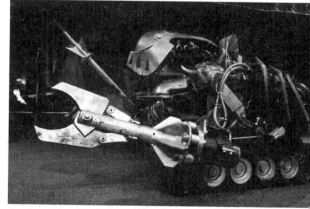

**Designed for destruction: Robot Wars®
house robot Sir Killalot**
Photo courtesy Mentorn Barraclough Carey Ltd.

No doubt the scientific-minded among you will want to know exactly how design inspiration leaped out of the robot arena and into your living room. Fair enough. First, the design ingenuity on display at any robot combat competition staggers the mind. Take weaponry designed for destruction, compound that with damage-defying defenses, add in the awe-inducing effect of brilliant engineering and fine art plus the wow factor of movie special effects, and multiply that by scores of robots. The stimulation is difficult for the human brain to absorb. So the brain processes this information as a challenge—and suddenly you're inspired. Want a better explanation than that? Then take a closer look at the mind-boggling elements that go into an effective and inspirational design.

> *Live where you fear to live.*
> *Destroy your reputation. Be notorious.*
> — *Rumi*

Wicked weapons and iron-clad defenses

In the universe of ideas, there are millions and billions of robot design possibilities...but without going into all the Carl Saganesque particulars, let's just say there has emerged from this universe a distinct pantheon of established design concepts. "The robots you see today are essentially all the same robots that showed up to Robot Wars® back in 1995—only bigger, meaner, faster, and they don't break," notes Gage Cauchois of Team Vladiator. Each design concept has its own complex set of strengths and weaknesses; there is no one that is all-powerful or impervious to destruction. "There isn't one robot that can handle everybody," says Team Fembot's Nola Garcia. "The trick is trying to combine design elements that will counter the best of various bots." The pantheon is not fixed, either—a newbie design could conceivably nudge aside some of the tried and true designs. So consider this a starter list of robot design concepts...and feel free to add your own.

Clampbot

Imagine if a lobster you were cooking leaped out of the pot, grabbed you by the nose and dragged you around the kitchen by it. That's the general idea behind most clampbots. Clamping alone will not win a match—but clamping and pushing, piercing, or sawing will. Many clampbots look like particularly pernicious crustaceans, with

Cute but deadly: Mecha Tentoumushi
Photo courtesy Winter family/ Photo by Becky Winter

prominent pincers—but Lisa Winter came up with an innovative approach to the clamp concept with her deceptively cute ladybug bot, Mecha Tentumoushi. "It's very fast and captures other robots under its shell so they can't go away," she explains. "Inside there's a grinding wheel like a saw blade that cuts into them." Another breakthrough clamp design is Derek Young's Complete Control, which grabs its opponents from above and struts around the arena with its hapless foe dangling from its steely clutches. Degrading for the opponent? Naturally. Entertaining for the audience? Absolutely.

Clusterbots/Multibots

Divide and conquer is the operative principle behind a clusterbot. It's a science fiction horror scenario: one robot divides into two or more sub-bots and surrounds its prey. Andrew Lindsey teamed up his robot Spike with former rival Tony Buchignani's Wedge of Doom to form a multibot for the first BattleBots®. "The plan was for the faster and more maneuverable Wedge of Doom to intercept the other robot, block and distract them while Spike got in position to use its lifting claw to flip the opponent over," recalls Andrew. "That was one of the quickest and cleanest fights I've witnessed or been in, and one of a very few examples of effective multibot strategy." The multibot approach has diabolical appeal, but opinion remains, well, divided on the merits of clusterbots. Team Díotóir's Pete Redmond counts among his favorites Gemini, "a clusterbot and the first of its kind on Robot Wars® in the U.K. It is hard to build a powerful robot within the weight limitations, but an amazing feat to build two powerful robots and keep the combined weight within the limits!" But according to bot builder and fan Dave Thau, the clusterbot concept didn't go over so well with some fans in BattleBots® season three. "People booed the clusterbots, because when they split apart there are really two bots against one in the arena—and there are rules about that."

Cutters

There goes the neighborhood: Razer hits the streets
Photo courtesy Team Razer/ Photo by Vincent Blood

Drills and chainsaws are dangerous tools indeed. But cutting implements that could kill a human being often don't stand a fighting chance against a robot. "Things like saws or drills generally don't make good weapons because they're designed for precise work," explains Team Ziggo's Jonathan Ridder. "In robot combat you're not going to get the chance to inflict damage with those things— the bots aren't going to stand still for you." Inertia Labs' Reason Bradley concurs: "There are a lot of saws that go into the arena, but they don't really do much." As with any robot design principle, however, there are some notable exceptions to this one. The painfully gradual piercing motion of Razer's flexible, horn-like weapon punctures opponents' armor and confidence—and captivates the crowd in the process. Hypno-Disc has a similarly mesmerizing effect on audiences; as it gains inertia, its signature spiral sawtoothed disc hits top speeds and lays waste to the opposition.

Flippers/Lifters

When one robot flips for another, it's certainly not out of love. Robots with flipping or lifting mechanisms treat their opponents to unwelcome airborne joyrides with very hard landings. In the fall, an opponent's armor can be damaged and key internal com-

Toro hits up Diesector
Photo courtesy BattleBots, Inc.®/ Photo by Daniel Longmire

ponents shaken loose. Opponents dread flips; the audience can't get enough of them. "It's basically Toro's pneumatic flipping arm and flipping ability that make him impressive out there," says Reason Bradley, builder of flipper extraordinaire Toro. "When there are robots that really get violent action happening in the arena, the audience really enjoys the show a lot more. When Toro drives into something, the other robot flies in the air and lands who knows where. He's a pretty rugged robot—a well-balanced young lad." Toro and champion lifters like BioHazard have changed the sport, forcing their opponents to consider incorporating into their own designs self-righting mechanisms, low ground clearance, and the capacity to function upside down. "If you get flipped over and you lose, it's a major design flaw," notes Ziggo's Jonathan Ridder.

Impact bots/Pounders

Getting the axe, getting hammered, getting picked on—these expressions take on a whole new meaning when an impact bot enters the

ards and win the match. Furry but ferocious Díotóir is a testament to the staying power of a good shoving strategy. "Díotóir's weapon is very complex and unreliable at the moment, so the high torque of Díotóir's drive and its ability to push other robots around has been its biggest strength," builder Pete Redmond explains. "The pit hazard [in Robot Wars®] is more of a problem for fast robots. I designed Díotóir for torque rather than speed. Díotóir is not really fast enough to accidentally drive into the pit but usually is strong enough to push others in to it."

Spinners/Spinbots/ Inertia bots

The power of inertia is enough to make your head spin—and send robot parts flying all over the arena. "Centrifugal weapons are becoming more popular because of the amount of rotational inertia they can store," explains Grant Imahara of Team Deadblow. "Early in Robot Wars® everyone thought the wedge was the one to have, but now people are seeing the benefits of spinning robots." By storing up energy with each successive rotation, inertia bots can turn against their enemies with formidable force. Whether they revolve on a vertical or horizontal axis, spinners have the power to injure even the most heavily armored bots. "You can get them spinning pretty fast," notes bot builder and engineer Dave Thau. "If one was coming at you and you tried to counter that force directly, it would definitely do you damage."

Horizontal spinners

These robots may resemble spinning tops, but don't be fooled—these killers are not to be toyed with. Ever since Blendo literally tore up the competition in the early years of Robot Wars®, horizontal spinners have been slashing and burning their way to the top of the heap. Horizontal spinners add insult to injury, as Jonathan Ridder of cham-

arena. Impact bots corner their enemies or strand them on hazards, then proceed to pound the daylights out of them. One of the first such pounders was Thor, a proverbial hammer of the gods with a Viking flair for vengeance. Thor inspired middleweight champ Deadblow, which has proved itself dangerously handy around the arena with its fast, pointed hammer. A new pounder, the Judge, is hitting the superheavyweight scene hard. "The Judge had a hammer that would totally destroy you if it hit you," says Vladiator's Gage Cauchois approvingly. Beware also robots with an axe to grind—including Shunt, the Robot Wars® house robot. "We were winning a fight once when Shunt came in to spice things up a little," recalls Team Díotóir's Pete Redmond. "He hit the circuit breakers with his axe, disabling Díotóir."

Pushbots

The pushbot paradigm is straight out of sumo wrestling: if you can shove your opponents around long and hard enough, you can best them in a fight. Sumo bot competitions take weapons out of the equation

He's no pushover: Chomp!
Photo courtesy Roger Korus/ Photo by Roger Korus

entirely; sumo robots are autonomous pushbots, programmed to shove opponents out of the ring. Robotica® also tests remote-controlled robots' pushing power with The Gauntlet, which requires robots to ram their way though walls of glass, paint cans, bricks, concrete blocks, and finally, a bank vault. In fact, most combat robot competitions involve an underlying pushbot principle: Even if all their weapons fail, robots with pushing power can thrust opponents against the arena haz-

pion spinner Ziggo fame explains: "The air blows out all the scraps left over on the floor of the arena from previous battles, clearing a path for me and spitting debris at my opponent." The devastation Ziggo, Mauler 51-50, Mouser Super Mecha Catbot, and other horizontal spinners leave in their wake gives the crowd an undeniable thrill, coupled with a renewed appreciation for the Lexan® shield between

Very bad kitty: April Davis fixes Mouser Mecha-Catbot
Photo courtesy April Davis/Photo by Fon Davis

the audience and the arena. These spinners tear up opponents and hazards—and occasionally themselves in the process. "There are 20-30 [horizontal] inertia robots out there that will do phenomenal damage, but they'll destroy themselves in the process—so you don't see them but once, and they're not really well-known," points out Inertia Labs' Reason Bradley. "But a bunch of them could filet other bots." Carlo Bertocchini knows the destructive power of inertia firsthand—the lethal spinning arms of shufflebot Son of Whyachi ripped two panels from his longtime heavyweight champ BioHazard in a surprise upset. "The spinning robots are something to worry about not because they win occasionally, but because they destroy themselves and their opponent in the course of a match," says Carlo. "So I know that even if I win the match, I'm going to have a lot of repair work to do."

Vertical spinners

Vertical spinners look like giant Ninja weapons on wheels, and they're every bit as dangerous as they appear—even with a deceptive name like Sunshine Lollibot. Jim Smentowski's vertical spinner Nightmare is perhaps one of the most aptly-named bots ever to cast its sinister shadow across the arena; it earns its name by leaving opponents belly up and broken down after just a single

We have liftoff: Backlash sends Carnage flying
Photo courtesy Bot Bash LLC/ Photo by John Kittelsrud

hit. "I went up against Nightmare, and I think Nightmare damaged BioHazard more than the [horizontal] spinners," says Carlo Bertocchini. "Nightmare ripped a big gouge in the panel that took a lot of time to fix." Tall vertical spinners like Nightmare and Backlash lack the low center of gravity that helps keep most bots grounded, so it takes an expert driver to keep them upright. "Backlash constantly looks like it's about to topple over, but it doesn't," says bot builder/fan/engineer Dave Thau. "Jim Smentowski's a great driver."

Walkers/Shufflebots

Walkers are what most people imagine when you say "robot": a machine that moves like a human, with stubby legs and flat feet. Some walkers are surprisingly fast on their feet, but their movement is generally more complex, less stable, and slower than a set of wheels. For all these reasons, walking robots are prone to winding up prone in fights. But the audience has an instinctive empathy for walkers, both as underdogs and as hapless humanoids playing a machine's game: it's like watching a person being pitted against a car. To give walkers a leg up on their wheeled competition, walkers have even been granted the robot equivalent of a golfer's handicap in BattleBots®—but that may soon come to an end as the rules are revisited. Many builders have moved on to other designs already. "I like all the walking robots, but I haven't built a walker since 1998," says Christian Carlberg, who has built two walking robots in addition to champs Minion and OverKill. "It's a good engineering challenge, but now I'm reinventing tried-and-true designs." Still, some hefty new speed-walkers have been giving wheeled bots a run for their prize money. "I think speed-walkers that are more like armored safes, like Drill Zilla, may evolve into a class of their own," says Team Robot Widows' Gillian Blood. "They are truly scary and unique."

Wedges

One of the most hotly contested of all design options, the wedge is both admired and reviled for being a simple, effective design. These robots are essentially pushbots resembling a wedge of cheese, with a nose that slides under opponents before shoving them up against hazards. Many have wheels on the top and bottom, so they are equally effective right-side-up and upside-down. "In physics, there are essentially four key machines—the inclined plane, wheel, pulley, and wedge—so it wasn't so hard to decide on a wedge design," explains Gage Cauchois, who built the first wedge-shaped bot, La Machine, with Greg Munson and Trey Roski. La Machine raised a ruckus both in the ring and out of it; builders rushed to create the next generation of aggressive wedges, while others scrambled to invent bots that would put wedges out of commission. "A lot of people hate wedges, for the same reasons a lot of people hate Microsoft: because it's boring, and it's way too suc-

Wedge of Doom
Photo courtesy BattleBots, Inc.®/Photo by Daniel Longmire

cessful," explains Armored Robotics' Rik Winter. Ah, but that's the beauty of the thing, claim the many fans of champions Atomic Wedgie and Wedge of Doom. But many others beg to differ. "Basing your entire design on this old but tired method is just tasteless at this point in the game," says Team Carnivore's Ilya Polyakov. "Blade Runner was designed specifically against bots such as these." So who's the ultimate winner in this debate? The audience—the debate brings an added element of drama to the arena.

. . . and now for something
completely different

It's a jungle out there: Super ChiaBot
Photo courtesy Robot Action League/ Photo by Will Wright

Certain robot designs both delight and stump us: when pressed to describe them, we're left babbling incoherently: "There's this thingy, and it kind of thrusts out like this, and it moves like it's underwater only it's not, and it seems very, very sharp..." Fact is, builders are inventing robots faster than we can coin terminology to describe them. "If you saw Ginsu on a table, you may not know what it is—you just don't want to be around it," explains Trey Roski of his and Greg Munson's latest creation. "It even scares me to turn the darn thing on!" Some designs are even hard for their originators to define. Take for example one of Ilya Polyakov's dream bot project descriptions: "If you put the Jaws of Life on a shrimp and mix in a little reptilian tail, you would have it." Now if this sounds improbable to you, just remember that strange things can and do happen in the arena—many-armed robot deity Diesector, mighty menacing Mechadon, and leafy (yes, leafy!) Chiabot, to name just a few. These and other iconoclastic robots by (respectively) engineer Donald Hutson, special effects master Mark Setrakian, and SimCity originator Will Wright and daughter Cassidy Wright have a most peculiar effect on us; they short-circuit the logic center of our brains, leaving us slack-jawed and blinking in disbelief. The judges don't always know what to make of certain design innovations, either—at least, not at first. "Will Wright has come up with many inventions that have forced a rule change," says Armored Robotics' Rik Winter with admiration. "He made a robot with really sticky double-sided duct tape and magnets. He would just let the magnets fly off into your robot, then drive around you and goo everything up." No, don't bother to adjust your television dial: these robots are for real.

> *It's not the size of the dog in the fight—it's the size of the fight in the dog.*
> *— Mark Twain*

Pick on someone
your own size

Ever wish you could be reincarnated as the biggest, baddest kid on the block? Or that you could be a lightning-fast, scrappy little kid all over again? Then build yourself a bot. The arena is the one place where you get to find out what it's like to be the little one that wins big, or the giant that becomes truly mighty. Robots come in all sizes, from the downright hulking to the remarkably compact. But it must be said that lightweights are heavy hitters in the arena—they can inflict serious damage on heavily armored machines, and put on a spectacular show as they dodge hazards. With their speed and often razor-sharp weaponry, many lightweights could easily take out humans twice their size (so don't go picking a fight with one!). As for the big ones:

Television really doesn't do them justice. "On TV, they zoom in on the little ones so it seems like they're all the same size," says Toro builder Reason Bradley. "People are always surprised by how big Toro is. People come up and say, 'Holy smokes, this thing's HUGE!' And it's not huge, but it *is* 325 pounds."

Weighty matters

If all bots are equally fierce, does size really matter? Absolutely, says Armored Robotics' Rik Winter. "The weaponry and playing field interact very differently for heavyweights," he observes.

Team Razer gets giddy after making the weight
Photo courtesy of Team Razer/Photo by Vincent Blood

"It's a different sport depending on your class. It's actually more dangerous for heavyweights, because they get caught on hazards. But they don't have to worry about weight, so they can use the nice heavy steel armor and weaponry. It's really hard for lightweights to have weapons that can do damage because of the weight restrictions." Each robot competition has specific weight limits, and builders have to design around them—or endure the torture of making last-minute design changes to meet the weigh-in requirements. "The most cardinal sin a robot builder can commit is designing without a weight limit in mind," says Team Deadblow's Grant Imahara. "You should know the density of aluminum and steel by heart so you can estimate weight accurately. It's horrible to have to cut parts out of your robot at the last minute because it's overweight." Accurate weight calculations are a point of pride: any builder who can anticipate a robot's weight within a few pounds of the initial schematics has undeniably fierce engineering kung fu.

Robot diets

Choosing a weight class rather than letting it choose them keeps builders honest about what needs to be on their bot, and what doesn't. Robots carrying a lot of dead weight are likely to become dead weight altogether in the arena. "Adding pounds is like spending your money—you have to be careful where you spend your weight," explains Carlo Bertocchini, builder of heavyweight BioHazard. "You can spend it on cool appendages and cosmetic appeal, but those things don't help you win. The builders have done a great job if they can create a cool robot that still wins." Certain cool design features actually serve a weight reduction function. Ever notice that some robots have a perforated pattern on their appendages? Those holes are more than just cosmetic—they're a clever way for a builder to keep the robot's weight down. To get heavyweight Toro down to fighting weight, Reason Bradley and Alexander Rose cut out discs of metal from Toro's powerful pneumatic arm. The resulting pattern of circles running down the arm make a (quite literally) striking design—and Toro has been making a ruckus in the arena ever since.

Few topographical boundaries can rival the frontiers of the mind. - Salman Rushdie

Robot personality types

Combat robots are like snowflakes; no two are exactly alike. "Building a robot is a like a fractal," explains Greg Munson, builder and co-founder of BattleBots®. "There are innumerable possible choices at every juncture." Ultimately, each builder must navigate these design choices according to an internal compass. So even when builders are working with the same tried-and-true concept, their designs end up looking and behaving differently. This is not just a matter of machining or wiring—it's a matter of personality. "In a way, a robot is like a self-portrait," explains builder and BattleBots® co-founder Trey Roski. "The way they look, move, and perform—that's all an extension of the builder."

Dr. Joanne meets her dreambot, Y2K2
Photo courtesy of BattleBots®, Inc., Symborg Labs, and Dr. Joanne Pransky

When you watch a robot in action, you're witnessing a lifetime's learning and experience. A robot reveals a lot about the builders' own influences: some look like animals (cats and scorpions are perennial favorites); some could only be the offspring of science fiction movie monsters; many incorporate toys, especially fire engines and Barbie® doll heads; some appear to be runaway appliances from an industrial supply warehouse; some could be mutant iMacs®. We respond instinctually to the familiar human qualities their builders give them: that one seems elegant, that one makes us laugh, that one we wouldn't want to run into alone in a dark alley. If you were to psychoanalyze these robots (and believe it or not, Dr. Joanne Pransky actually has), certain personality types begin to emerge. Below are some of the more high-profile types. If you don't see a robot personality type listed here that suits you, then maybe it's time to get started on your own robot, and make your robot presence known.

Martial artists

Most robots are built to win, or at least put on an unforgettable show—and that requires attention to function as well as form. "I try to make robots that will not break," says Gage Cauchois of the design philosophy behind La Machine, Vlad the Impaler, and Vladiator. These machines were all shockmounted to survive the martial arts feats that have made them famous: richocheting off spiked walls, slamming against opponents, rolling fearlessly over the saws. La Machine became an instant crowd favorite not because of how it looks (think wedge with a punk rock edge), but because of the attitude it dished out in the arena. "La Machine was all about aggressive driving," recalls Team Sinister's Mark Setrakian. "Trey just drove the stuff out of that thing—during the melee, it would be stacking the other robots in the corner." Other robots have also elevated performance to an art form—when Toro and Little Sister start tossing their opponents around the arena, it's like watching a pneumatic ballet. This seemingly spontaneous action is the result of careful engineering and difficult design decisions. "For me, form follows function for the most part," explains Inertia Labs' Reason Bradley. "We try to add on details, but we have to watch the weight. The tails on Toro are functional, but we try to make them look good. We brushed the armor, which is what gives it that sheen—and it also disguises any scratches. I would like more curves on Toro, but the design comes together with that pneumatic arm."

Engineering masterminds

An astounding piece of engineering doesn't necessarily require adornment—take for example Carlo Bertocchini's sleek BioHazard, with its precision-machined armor and breakthrough lifting arm. "There's nothing on BioHazard that's there just to look cool," says Carlo.

Engineering that will Deadblow your mind
Photo courtesy Grant Imahara

Before: Díotoír cavorting naked on the grass
Photo courtesy Team Díotoír/Photo by Pete Redmond

"The form of BioHazard is strictly after the function of winning a match." Precision machining also distinguishes Grant Imahara's Deadblow, with its gleaming, tapered hammer and armor with a futuristic, streamlined groove pattern that is perhaps best described as Alien Art Deco. But in the arena, that pneumatic hammer and detailed armor become a blur of motion; they are as efficacious as they are impressive. Pioneering spinner Blendo was made from a wok instead of titanium panels, but it is nonetheless an impressive feat of engineering. As it revolves on its vertical axis, it deflects opponents' blows and turns their own force back against them—a brilliant application of a fundamental physics principle that elevated the level of competition (as well as a few competitors).

Masters of disguises

Looks can be deceptive when it comes to robots; some don't look like robots at all. Certain builders take great pains to disguise their robot's machine nature—think of Chiabot's greenery, or Díotoír's grinning, furry mug, or the doll atop the fire engine in Buddy Lee Stay in Your Seat. "I knew we needed something unusual, something entertaining—this was TV," says Nola Garcia of Buddy Lee's distinctive design. "So one day we were walking by a window display with all these kids' pedal cars and I

After: Díotoír in battle garb
Photo courtesy Team Díotoír/Photo by Pete Redmond

thought: That's it—let's do a fire engine! The guys on Team Loki said 'Oh, how nice, how cute,' but I don't think they thought of Buddy Lee as competition. Then after he won a couple of matches, they started saying, 'Maybe there's a real robot under that little fire truck after all!' After the first match, we put a BandAid on Buddy Lee, just to have some fun. When he made it through the next match, we put a sling on his arm. Then in the next match, he had a bandage on his head…the crowd loved it."

Artistically inclined

The arena is one place where technical wizardry meets artistic flair. Zach Bieber's Diablo is a natural favorite among Kustom car fanatics, with a diabolical custom paint job (painted by Zach himself) and a muscular build that would do a GTO proud. Fon Davis' Mouser Mecha Super Catbot wins over cat lovers and sci-fi buffs alike; it's part cute pink cartoon cat, and

The artists in their studio: Fon and April Davis perfecting Mouser Mecha-Catbot
Photo courtesy April Davis

part evil cybercat with a glowing red eye. Team Coolrobots also causes a stir at competitions by introducing distinctive, championship-ready new robots and reinventing longtime champions like Minion. "Minion got people's attention because it looked cool, in addition to being powerful and fast," explains Coolrobots' Christian Carlberg. "At first Minion was all chromed silver, which was really eye-catching. This year it was re-designed as a self-righter with more powerful weapons. I couldn't chrome the second version, and it ended up being a silverish grey I hated. So I decided to make it all black, and that really surprised and pleased the fans."

Showstoppers

Many robots could easily be mistaken for sculptures—until you see them in action. "[Shane Washburn's] Scorpion was one of the most spectacular designs I'd ever seen," recalls Armored Robotics' Rik Winter. "When it walked into the arena, you could hear the collective gasp. It was all hydraulic, with a big stinger—it was designed as art, but it could run and fight and hold up well." The Robot Action League's Will Wright calls this scene-stealing effect the "It's alive!" factor, and pioneering

What in the...?!: Mechadon makes quite an entrance
Photo courtesy BattleBots, Inc.®/ Photo by Garry Gay

builders including Will himself, Ian Smith, Derek Young, Donald Hutson, and Mark Setrakian have got it down to a science. "I decided in 1996 that if I was going to have to build something new every time in order to win, it would be more fun to make something as different as I could from anything else and just eliminate the need to win from my design criteria," explains Team Sinister's Mark Setrakian. Mark's approach has yielded astounding robots The Snake and Mechadon, which can only be described as art with a vengeance. These iconoclastic creations have left lasting impressions on audiences and inspired many builders, including Christian Carlberg, Ilya Polyakov and Reason Bradley. As Buddy Lee Stay in Your Seat's Nola Garcia says, "Some designs make you kick yourself in the rear and think: Why didn't I do that? It's great to imitate what's been done, but you've got to let your mind wander too." Is it risky to attempt something so completely new? Of course. But creative risks keep the sport exciting for builders and audience alike.

There is no accident, just as there is no beginning and no end.
— Jackson Pollock

Robot reincarnation

If builders are lucky, they get a few minutes' break from building their bots—and that's while their bots are duking it out in the arena. Otherwise, they're either building new ones or rebuilding existing ones. The trick is knowing when to do what. "The question is: Do I abandon the existing robot and go with something more interesting, or keep working on the old one?" says Team Coolrobots' Christian Carlberg. "That's the trap of a successful robot: you want to keep improving it, but also come back with other designs. Essentially you want to have your cake and eat it too."

The clean slate club

Some robot-builders don't believe in reincarnation. "It's really hard to design a robot for one thing, and then redesign it with a totally different purpose—you'd be cutting parts out, and trying to patch other ones on," explains Reason Bradley of Inertia Labs. "We vowed not to do that anymore after Rhino—now we just start over. If you wanted to change Toro and put in a different weapon, that would be hard to do. People log thousands and thousands of hours redesigning their bots, but we've changed our whole style of building robots to where we're pretty fast at building a new one from scratch."

Robots with nine lives

Others take the nine lives attitude towards reincarnation; they allow their bots a finite number of revivals before they move on to the next incarnation. "No robot ever reaches perfection—it's an incremental, evolutionary process," observes Grant Imahara of Deadblow fame. "Still, you can't always keep your robot fresh and interesting by just making improvements. Sometimes you need to start from scratch. Plus the competition has gotten so much better lately that what worked in one tournament won't necessarily the next time around."

Mini Inferno after a mini makeover
Photo courtesy the Infernolab /Photo by Jason Bardis

Bionic bots

The Six Million Dollar Man approach works for some builders (you know: "We can rebuild him. We have the technology…to make him better, stronger, faster than before…"). Jason Bardis of Team Inferno is one believer in bionic bots. "After every event that one of my bots survives, it gets upgraded," he says. "I've never made it through an event without some sort of failure, so that gets addressed and resolved before the next one. My bots gradually become more and more robust and more and more successful, until they're torn apart beyond repair by some killer bot—which is usually Ziggo. My motivation is to come back next time and get farther than the previous event." Like Jason, Lisa Winter has no fear of fights—even though it takes her about eight months to get Mecha Tentoumushi repaired and ready for the next competition. "I don't get sad if my bot gets torn up 'cause I can just make a new version or fix it," she says. "Battle damage is an opportunity for new ideas and to make improvements to your design."

The Godfathers

And then there are the Godfather bots: They've already had at least twice the life span of their contemporaries, and still they'll make you an offer you can't refuse. Ziggo is one such bot; he takes out hits on his opponents all the time, but other robots can't seem to get close enough to cause him any fatal damage. Arena hazards scarcely phase Gage Cauchois, who built the diehard La Machine, Vlad the Impaler, and Vladiator, and is working on a Vlad sequel that will no doubt chew nails for breakfast. Then there's BioHazard—it only seems to sustain minor robot flesh wounds, so Carlo Bertocchini can get away with carrying hardly any tools to competition. This begs the question: Is the BioHazard Team up to some kind of robot juju? Not if you believe Carlo: "I originally built the robot in 1995 and competed for the first time in '96, and if I hadn't been forced to make repairs and improvements it wouldn't still be competitive." Hmmm…we're still suspicious.

The future belongs to those who believe in the beauty of their dreams.
— Eleanor Roosevelt

Future forward

Here's a safe prediction for you: The future will have lots of robots in it. Heard that one before, have you? Well, but this time it's really going to happen—and sooner rather than later. This is not idle speculation; this information comes straight from robot builders, who are so busy inventing the future they have precious little time left over for idleness or speculation. But we managed to tear them away from their hot pursuit of the 22nd century long enough to ask a few crucial questions about future robots, namely: What will they be like? Where will they hang out? And most importantly, will they do our laundry?

Evolution in action

If you're amazed by what you see in robot combat competitions, just wait until next year. According to builders, the pace of robot evolution is increasing exponentially with each competition. To put that in human terms: If you can imagine that robots on the whole have already evolved to the equivalent of Australopithecus, we could be seeing a fully-fledged Homo Sapiens within a year or two. "The biggest factor in our success has been the creativity and endless effort of the robot builders," explains BattleBots® co-founder and bot builder Greg Munson. "Although our safety restrictions and rules are pretty tight, at every new competition we see beautifully designed and constructed BattleBots®. Builders are really putting their personalities into them, using color and paint, exotic materials and motors and coming up with devious weapon designs to foil their opponents. More and more we're seeing two robots go in and one come out in a bag. That's exciting—and the best is yet to come." Run Amok's Mark Joerger confirms this prediction. "In just the last few months the sport has seen a great many new developments in weaponry and drive systems," he says. "Some of the most creative minds on the planet are working to develop a combination of design elements that will send the competition running in panic toward the arena exits."

Highest tech

With robot competitions getting so many minds racing, breakthroughs are to be expected—especially as information and key components become more widely available. "The recent release of information and the standardization of basic components (radios, motors, wheels, speed controllers, etc.) allow those new to the sport to build a robust entry more easily than we could a few years ago," explains Team Inferno's Jason Bardis. "I think robots will become more humanoid as mechanisms, power sources and actuators become more powerful, yet more

efficient and smaller. There
will also be more elegant
control schemes than joy-
sticks and switches, such as
wearable suits and devices
that read eye movements or
brainwaves." If that sounds
implausible, consider the
amazing robot innovations
that are already on the
drawing table thanks to
emerging technology.
"Currently people are get-

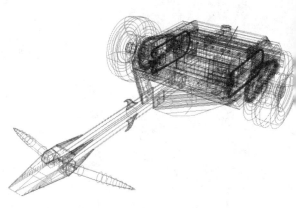

Blade Runner's immaculate conception
Photo courtesy Team Carnivore/ Photo by Ilya
Polyakov

ting into composites, advanced alloys, and cool microcontroller technology," reports Team Carnivore's Ilya Polyakov. "Eventually the sport will
catch up with the absolute latest in anything around. So I can only
assume the second a cold fusion reactor comes on the market, it will be
used in robot combat!"

Cutting the
apron strings

With all these smarts at their disposal, bots will become more independ-
ent-minded. They won't be relying on their remote controllers so much
to help them get around—builders are already incorporating on-board
systems to alleviate drivers' remote control repetitive stress. "Robots are
going to become more like real autonomous robots," explains Team
Sinister's Mark Setrakian. "On-board control systems will take some of
the complexities out of robot driving and make it the responsibility of the
robot, and the firing of weapons might be automated. That could increase
the danger of people getting hurt." Jason Bardis concurs. "Combat robots
will become more and more deadly every event as new ideas and technologies come into play." But robots won't necessarily be naughty by

Dangerous dudes: Dr. Inferno Jr. and Jason Bardis
Photo Courtesy the Infernolab/
Photo by Jason Schock /Daily
Nexus

nature, predicts bot builder and engineer Dave Thau: "I think there will be communicating robots that participate in robot team sports. Maybe they'd give each other words of encouragement: 'That's not so bad!' 'Looks like your right wheel is a little off.' 'Nice try!'" This is not as outlandish as it sounds—well, maybe it *is* as outlandish as it sounds, but it's in the works nonetheless. "There's already robot soccer, like Robocup®," says Carlo Bertocchini of Team BioHazard. "Their goal is to build a team of robot players that would be competitive with human players by the year 2050."

Robot haunts

Robots are becoming regular social butterflies. They're always out and about: underwater cleaning up marine messes humans have made, on minefields defusing live landmines, in nuclear reactors doing maintenance, in quarantined wards at your local hospital delivering meds, and inside burning buildings practicing rescue strategies. Basically, they're everywhere you don't want to be. But there are a growing number of robot combat competitions where humans and robots can unwind together. There are air and water robot competitions in addition to the ones on the ground, and distance robotics may soon give us the ability to compete with robots on other continents from the comfort of our living rooms (several functioning distance robotics art projects already exist in Japan).

Sizing up the competition

There may soon be competitions you can attend with robots that make Gigantor look small. "I think what is going to happen inevitably with robots is a dramatic increase in scale," explains Robot Wars® creator Marc Thorpe. "With sumo wrestlers, there's a limit to how big they can be—you can only get people up to 500 pounds or so. But with robots, there are no practical limits. Robots sponsored by huge corporations can weigh 20 tons and compete in the desert on closed circuit TV, if that is what people would like to see. And I do think that is what they want to see.

Plucky little things

If you're an extremist by nature but lack the room in your basement for a tank, you might consider moving to the opposite end of the scale: tiny fighting bots. Mini sumo is already underway. "I constructed a miniature autonomous sumo robot for the Western Canadian Robot Games, but unfortunately that mini sumo competition did not run since none of the other competitors' robots worked properly," says Roger Korus, an 18-year-old autonomous bot builder. "But I wasn't upset, since my mini sumo bot was created mostly to try out more advanced micro-controllers. Now I'm constructing a new mini sumo robot, and so is my dad." If it's itty bitty jousting bots you're after, the wait may be a bit longer. "People have talked about mini BattleBots®, but I'm not sure how much fun that'd be to watch because you wouldn't have the impact of sounds or visible damage," explains Armored Robotics' Rik Winter.

Housebroken bots

We know what you're thinking: If there will be robots that can handle nuclear waste in the near future, surely there is one that can contend with your dirty socks. You're absolutely right (unless there's something we should know about your socks). "In Japan, there are already household robots," reports Team Ziggo's Jonathan Ridder. But you may not have to go to Japan to find yourself a robot valet. "I think the breed of automated house utility bots will eventually take off," says sumo bot builder Dion Brewington. "Robotic lawn mowers and vacuum cleaners have been out for some time now, and the accuracy and reliability of these are consistently improving. I think that as the exposure to robotics increases and the cost of the technology decreases, we will see more of this integrated into our society." Fifteen-year-old autonomous bot builder Alex Burke

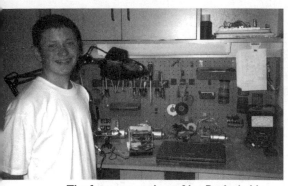

The future starts here: Alex Burke in his workshop
Photo courtesy Alex Burke/Photo by Patty Burke

isn't waiting around for it to happen—he's already working on a better robot lawn mower, and he conceives of burger-flipping robots and hotel bed-making robots in the not-so-distant future. So maybe you can ask him about a laundry robot, if you can catch him before he's completely engrossed in his next project: a kayak bot. "These things are already beginning to sound normal," remarks Team Fembot member and teen mentor Nola Garcia. "Our grandkids will think we were all living in such a primitive way before robots came along!"

Robots have feelings, too, you know: A chat with Dr. Joanne Pransky,

World's First Robotic Psychiatrist® and BattleBots® judge

Why does the world need a robotic psychiatrist?

After seeing the movie *Short Circuit* in May 1986, I couldn't help but think that it would only be a matter of time before robots would be a part of

our everyday lives. But I kept thinking, how are we going to program our robots to do the dishes when we can't even record *Sixty Minutes* on our VCRs while we're away? So, in June of 1986 I humorously billed myself as The World's First Robotic Psychiatrist®. I saw my mission as helping people to understand the

Dr. Joanne and robots in surgery
Photo courtesy of Computer Museum of Boston and Dr. Joanne Pransky/Photo by Steve Pike

issues that will arise in a world where highly skilled, competent, and sensitive robots will play an integral role. I thought then, as I still do now, that when robots are intelligent as humans, they may actually begin to have psychological problems after coexisting with us on a daily basis.

Exactly what is a robopsychiatrist anyway?

Well, I believe that in the future our relationship with robots will be similar to our relationships with pets. That means that we'll buy them clothes out of the Spiegel® Catalogue for Robots; pay for an extra seat on the airplane to have them fly with us; fight over who gets to keep them in a divorce suit; and if our robots get depressed, we may even take them to a robotic psychiatrist for a weekly family encounter session. That's where I come in.

But the robots of the future won't really have feelings, will they?

As a direct response to interacting with humans in an ever-changing environment, robots, like pets, will exhibit behaviors that will resemble human emotions. A robot may discover, for instance, that when all assigned tasks are not finished within a certain period of time, the owner's voice gets loud, his eyebrows point in, his fists clench, and his eyes narrow. Whenever the robot cooks a gourmet meal, however, its human housemates smile, their faces relax and their eyes open; the robot interprets this as a positive response. In a cybernetic system, robots will learn to respond to us the way we want or expect them to in order to please us. Their personality modules will allow them to smile if we humans make a joke, look sad if we leave them, and so on.

Dr. Joanne Pransky works for Sankyo Robotics and is the US Associate Editor of *Industrial Robot, Assembly Automation, and Sensor Review* [Dr.Joanne@robot.md]

The best way to predict your future is to create it.
— Peter Drucker

BOT SHOT

Nola Garcia de Quevedo: recruiter/mentor/bot builder

Team Fembot, Team Loki: Mercy Rueda, teammate

Robot credits:
   Buddy Lee Don't Play in the Street (LW)
   Buddy Lee Stay in Your Seat

Home base: Miami, FL

Bots aren't just for boys

My son got into robotics in high school, and I got involved as the team coordinator. I went to the first BattleBots® event, and I just knew I had to compete. So after I'd been the team manager for Team Loki for awhile, I said "I want to drive!" Finally one of the guys said, "You know, on a Nascar team, the person who changes the batteries isn't the driver." Now as my husband will tell you, you can never tell me *not* to do something. So that's when I decided to build and drive a robot. I knew Mercy, who's an electrical engineer, would be the perfect partner, so I said, "Come on, let's let people know that the guys aren't the only ones who can build and drive great robots! Let's show them we can do this!" The Team Loki guys were good sports, and helped us out with Buddy Lee Don't Play in the Street. But I don't think anyone really expected our bot would win two fights at BattleBots®—let alone beat Team Loki's Turbo! As a result more female robot builders are out there and doing great!

The kids are alright

This year the stands and the pits at BattleBots® were packed with families. It's terrific so many kids are getting involved with robot-building. I lead a team of 70 kids in the US FIRST robotics competition, and at one event the founder pointed out that kids know all about sports statistics, but most couldn't name five Nobel scientists. All that could change as robot sports popularize science. Trey and Greg [BattleBots® co-founders] are excited about the learning potential here, so they've given their support to BattleBots® IQ, a curriculum based on robot-building developed by Michael Bastoni and myself with the help of Alex Slocum at MIT. There are many skills involved: physics, chemistry, mathematics, research, budget management, accountability, teamwork and communication. This fall 25 teachers are piloting the program, and you'll see the results at BattleBots®. Business leaders are excited about what that means to the future work force for this country.

Nola, Mercy, and Buddy Lee
Photo courtesy BattleBots, Inc.®/ Photo by Daniel Longmire

A playground for the mind

I founded Starbot, a volunteer-run workshop where kids learn to build robots and other inventions. It's a playground for the mind. Kids from million-dollar homes and impoverished neighborhoods work together here, and about 50% of them are girls. None of them really think they could build a robot at first—but then they do, and they come away with such a sense of self-esteem and community. Recently I found out that one girl who is a brilliant high school engineering student has liver cancer, and she takes a bus two hours each way just to get to Starbot. When I mentioned this to another parent, he gave her a computer, printer, and e-mail access so she could work on designs from home when necessary. That's the difference robots can make. I've seen a lot of kids lives changed as a result of being involved with these robotics programs.

BOT SHOT

Jenny Smith, Gillie Blood, Fiona Mason:
avengers/bot builders

Team Robot Widows: Emma Cathcart, teammate

Robot credits:
Widow's Revenge

Home base: England

Sweet Revenge

JS: I got involved in robotic combat though my partner Geoff. I have to thank Geoff a great deal for his time and expertise. He was building his robot Scorpion, and needed a face painted on it—so I had a hand in that. The Widow's Revenge team really got together when a fellow competitor said that the girls should stop moaning and build one for ourselves—maybe then we would find out how difficult they are to build. So we did. It was a chance for the girls to prove that with a little help we could build one. We decided that being the first all female team that we would give our support to a charity. We chose the Breast Cancer Campaign. This was important, as most of us know someone touched by this disease. I would like to see more girls getting involved in robot building—there are not enough of us.

If you can't beat them

GB: After catching an episode of the first UK series of Robot Wars®, my husband Ian and his mate Simon (Fiona's boyfriend) built Razer, now a very famous robot on the Robot Wars® circuit. The same year that Razer was born so was our daughter Darcie-Mia. I've spent many a lonely night at home on my own, raising Darci and keeping the house whilst Ian was out in the shed with Simon building robots. A guy called Dorian from a team called the Morgue posted a conversation thread on the Robot Wars® Web site, asking if there were any robot widows out there. It was from here that Jenny, Fiona, and I got together and the idea of the Robot Widows team was born. Our motto is: "If you can't beat them, join them…and then beat them!"

Widow's Revenge (not pictured: Jenny Smith)
Photo courtesy Team Robot Widows/ Photo by E. Cathcart

A killer kitchen tool

FM: We're not sure how Widow's Revenge will do [in the Robot Wars®, UK series 5], but so far so good. Widow's Revenge has a fantastic and very menacing sharp-toothed rolling pin built by yours truly. It's got a spin to be proud of, and a rear disc-cutter if anyone wants to try our rear end! We have confidence that we will get through a few heats—and confidence goes a long way. We will learn by our mistakes, if need be. I most fear Razer because they are our other halves and they are desperate to rip us to shreds…what a surprise…but we know their capability too!

BOT SHOT

Michael Bastoni: teacher/bot builder

Plymouth North High School Allied Technology Program:
Andy Burgess, Adam Sternberg, David Cann, Russel Bozeck,
Elizabeth Verrochi, Michael Madden, Eric DeGiorgi,
Danny Kelley, Pat Kelley, Jack Riley, Kenneth Magno,
David Keay, Kevin Braun, Joseph Bastoni, James Stevens,
and Joseph Pizzarella, PNTA Engineering Team members

Robot credits:
Reactor (HW)
Gungnir
1998 US FIRST Chairman's Award

Home base: Plymouth, Massachusetts

Divine inspiration

In 1994, Agnes Hayes, a science teacher and retired nun, handed me a videotape of the US FIRST robot competition. I looked at that tape and said, "My god, this is amazing—a real a challenge for the mind that shows students, 'Hey, there's a use for that algebra, that geometry, that science.'" I approached Steve Verrochi, a young engineer who had told me that his company, Entergy, wanted to help out the schools. We presented our idea for a hands-on robotics/technology program to the station managers and they funded the effort. With help from the students, their parents and John Siever our Vice Principal, the Plymouth North High School Allied Technology program was up and running in less than a year. We took 12 students to the 1995 US FIRST competition in Florida and won rookie of the year.

A level playing field

There are no real high school robotics teachers out there—not in the traditional sense anyway. My students know that Old Mr. B hasn't got all the answers, and that I'm honest enough to admit it. They realize, "Now we *really* get to participate." My job is to model learning, not to teach. I show people what learning looks and feels like. As a learning tool, building robots puts everybody in the "How do I do this?" place. That's what BattleBots® does—puts all of us, teachers and students, together in the same boat.

We could be heroes

If we win, hey that's great, but this is about more than the event—it's about the process. It's about being in the game and we were in every game we played at Battlebots® (San Francisco, season 3.0). We didn't win, but our bot did everything it was supposed to. We learned a lot and the kids had the time of their lives. Afterwards, one of our drivers (11th grader Andy Burgess) told me how great it was hanging out in the pits

Michael Bastoni, Jack Riley, Andy Burgess, James Stevens, Danny Kelly, Pat Kelly, and Adam Sternberg with Reactor
Photo courtesy Michael Bastoni & Team PNTA/Photo by Eric Sternberg

with champs like Christian Carlberg, Mark Setrakian, and Carlo Bertocchini. He said, "You know, Mr. B., it was amazing; they treated us like equals." They look at these guys like gods, and there they were just talking robots together. Like I told Andy, they are equals—they're builders.

The digital sandbox

A lot of people ask me how I know this program is working. When it's 10:00 p.m. Sunday night at PNHS and I have to tell people, "I'm turning the lights out. I'm going home," I know it's working. I know it's working when other teachers are in a panic, wondering why all these kids are asking for passes to room 222. They think, "They must be playing video games." We don't have video games, but we are allowing kids to *play* with science, to really *experience* learning, and to follow their passions. We've built an environment that extends beyond the computers, the tools, and the robots—I like to think of my classroom as a digital sandbox.

BOT SHOT

Alex Burke: teenager/bot buff

Robot credits:
   FirstBot

Home base: West Frankfort, Illinois

Born: 1985

bow-wowed

Soon after I saw a robotics exhibit at the Smithsonian in 2nd grade, there was this class project where everyone was required to make a robot. Most kids made non-working models out of clay or tinfoil—but my dad helped me make a robotic dog out of a remote-controlled fire engine. Then in 6th grade, I made my first autonomous robot. I didn't use a kit—I collected information on the Internet, got some parts and started tinkering around. That's how I made FirstBot, a motion robot that could roll around on a table, detect the table's edges with its sensors and follow the motion of my hand.

Where there's smoke, there's Alex

At first I used aluminum a lot, until I found out the hard way that using a conductive material for electronics isn't always such a good idea. I must've fried two boards by doing stuff like that. Now I've got a workbench all set up in the garage so if something starts to catch fire, I can put it out before my mom notices the smoke. My mom deserves a lot of credit.

Screwing up is underrated

I don't think mistakes are such a bad thing because there is so much you can learn from having to correct them. Every mistake can give you an idea about the next robot you're going to build. Without my dad and his friend Jan Uhls, I might have given up on robotics—there are so many mistakes you have to make before your robot is finally finished. But they backed me up 100%. My dad isn't an engineer or anything—he

Alex with Firstbot
Photo courtesy Patty Burke/ Photo by Patty Burke

works in maintenance for a coal company—but after I started getting interested in robots, he got excited about them too and helped a lot.

More than one way to skin a cat

I mow lawns to earn money for robot parts, and at the moment I'm building a lawn-mowing robot. Other robot mowers are so expensive that the only people who can afford them are people who usually have gardeners to come in and do the work for them anyway. So I'm working on a model that people could afford. But I still have some work to do so it doesn't wind up mowing the driveway, or chasing the neighbor's cat.

Now that's what you call a self-starter

I'd like to get involved in autonomous robot combat—it's important to have an end goal like a competition to keep you focused and offer new challenges. But there's nothing like that around here [in rural southern Illinois]. There aren't any other kids into robots in my town. Some think it's a waste of time—they'd rather be playing basketball. Others think it's way beyond them, even though it's really not—they're just machines, there's no reason to be intimidated. I think they're missing out. It's my age group that's going to see robots become part of our everyday lives. Some people may be happy to just be the users of the technology, but I want to invent it.

BOT SHOT

Bob Pitzer: BotBash founder/bot builder

Web site: www.botbash.com

Team Raptor

Robot credits:

Thumper
WhipLash
W.L.O.W.
Alpha Raptor
Beta Raptor (LW)
Gamma Raptor
Tripulta Raptor (SHW)
Tripulta Raptor Mod 1
Carnage Raptor
Rippa Raptor

Home base: Phoenix, Arizona

Born: 1969

Toying around

I started a group called the UUVS (Unmanned Underwater Vehicle Society) while I was in college at the University of Florida. Our team built the first submarine for the AUVSI (Association for Unmanned Vehicle Systems International) submarine competition. That was my first robot. AUVSI is better known for its helicopter competition, but I still think the submarines are cooler. After graduating, I needed to find a new place to compete with my toys and got involved with a small local Phoenix competition named BotBash.

Homespun fun

When I first got involved with Bash, it was three robots and a 2' diameter chalk circle. With the help of builders such as Team Delta, Team Cool Robots, and Team Nightmare, it has grown a lot over the last four to five years. This year's competition will have over 70 robots. Not bad for a home-grown event, especially since we're not on TV. For me—and I'd say every

Team Raptor with Beta Raptor
Photo courtsey Team Raptor/Photo by Kelly Walterscheid

Bash competitor—it's all about having a good time. Win or lose, if everyone leaves happy that makes all the work worth it. In the near future, a bunch of smaller competitions will pop up around the country. At this point, we're just breaking the surface with this robot combat stuff. It's going to have an interesting future.

Having a bash

BotBash is typical of any other robot competition in that competing is actually only about 5% of the work. The bulk of a team's time is spent preparing to be there. Event days are very exciting with many parallel operations happening at once. There are people scurrying around the pits trying to fix their robots. The crowd is yelling and screaming at what's going on in the arena, and everyone's dealing with the Arizona heat. Getting all the logistics done ahead of time is a lot of work, but if I've done my job right I basically just walk around the event and try to look important. I have a really good crew to make it all happen. One of my favorite moments at last year's show was watching a brand new Backlash roll out and totally destroy the feared Carnage. Pieces were flying everywhere. The fight between Toe Crusher and Slappy the Squirrel was another great one—fire is always good.

chapter 4

Join the Fray

Leisure and the cultivation of human capacities are inextricably interdependent.
— *Margaret Mead*

The obsession begins innocently enough: You're channel-surfing and flying sparks catch your eye, or you notice a flyer for a local robot competition. Robots! Fighting! The appeal is undeniable. You begin to have regular dates with your television; you start lurking in robotics chat rooms. What began as idle curiosity soon turns into full-fledged intrigue. You might even pick up a book on the subject, and read all the way through to the fourth chapter. By now, there's no denying it: you're officially a bot buff.

Welcome to the club. There are millions of us bot buffs around the world, yet there's a distinct camaraderie that gives us a sense of familiarity—kinship, even. Just check out bot combat competitions, local robotics societies and school robotics programs, and you'll see what we mean. The distinction between players and fans is not as clear as it is with other sports; builders are fans themselves, and fans often become builders. You don't need to know a secret handshake to join. As long as you've got an active imagination, an appreciation for mean machines, and a sporting attitude, you're in. So pick a venue, any venue, and make it yours.

The secret of genius is to carry the spirit of the child into old age, which means never losing your enthusiasm.
— Aldous Huxley

Step right up

People who think they've seen it all before are in for a shock at their first robot competition. There is no "been there, done that" when it comes to robots, because they are too new to the world and there is no limit to what they could do. But don't take our word for it—go see for yourself. In addition to the robot combat competitions on TV, there are smaller events happening in arenas, schools, and maybe a parking lot near you. Televised events like BattleBots® and Robot Wars® have also grown so big they're being held several times a year, and may soon begin to produce local or regional spin-off events that you can attend in person. Here are just a few options to get you started.

Go sumo

No, we don't mean scantily clad 400-pound guys with a penchant for pushing each other around. We're talking about scantily clad seven-pound autonomous robots with a *program* for pushing each other around. Robosumo is a rare and fascinating opportunity for humans to see what robots might do if left to their own devices. 18-year-old Canadian sumo and mini sumo bot builder Roger Korus first encountered sumo competitions at 16, and has been hooked ever since. "I got my dad to drive me down to the Western Canada Robot Games in 1999, and what really intrigued me was the sumo competition," he recalls. "I don't know exactly what it was, but there was something neat about two autonomous robots, duking it out Robato-a-Robato." The intriguing mechanical challenges and high-impact matches have lured many reknowned bot builders into robosumo. "I may be biased, because I was involved with it myself, but it's a really cool competition," says Team BioHazard's Carlo Bertocchini. "You put two robots in a five-foot circle, and they try to push each other out. These robots are autonomous, which means there's no radio control; it's all on-board computing." This computer system enables a sumo bot to sense the opponent's position, and devise a successful shoving strategy—much to the audience's amazement and delight. "The robots have sensors that can distinguish the white line [around the edge of the ring] from the black and are set up to avoid falling out of the ring," explains sumo bot builder Dion Brewington.

School programs

Gearing up for BattleBots IQ®: Nola Garcia, Evan Dammiano, Trey Roski, Ken Magno, Casey Visco, Brandon Gunn, Russ Bozek, Jim Stevens, Eric DeGiorgi, Tim Dwyer, Colleen Roski, Tine Munson, Kevin Braun, Andy Burgess, Greg Munson, Michael Bastoni and supporters
Photo courtesy Michael Bastoni/Photo by Tamson Burgess

If there isn't already a robotics program at your local high school or college, then it's high time somebody makes one happen (hint, hint!). Follow the lead of Team Díotoír's Pete Redmond. "We are trying to generate more interest and get schools and colleges interested, as it really is a great way to learn about engineering," he reports. "Robot Wars® has a lot of fans in Ireland, but we are the only ones who have built robots—so far." There's more to be learned from bots than engineering, as high school teacher and Reactor builder Michael Bastoni points out. "Robotics teaches students science, math, communication, visualization—all sorts of transferable skills that go well beyond building the bot," he says. Team Fembot member and teen mentor Nola Garcia agrees. "A robotics curriculum deals with math and science, but also: how do you get to decision? How do you market the team to sponsors? How do you budget? What kinds of safety guidelines do you need?" she says. "Robots will be a fact of life soon, and the kids that are prepared for that are ahead of the game."

What have robots done for you lately?
(We asked teens at Miami's Starbot Foundation; here's what they have to say on the subject.)

"The Starbot Foundation, home to Ramtech 59 and 4 teams of Battlebots® IQ, has opened my eyes to a whole new world. I ride in my car now, on the way to school or returning home from Starbot, and I no longer see trucks, buses, and streetlights. I see deeper, into the mechanics of machines, to their gears and the streaming electrons that power them. Everything I see or hear is transformed into a chaotic engineering design. Never before have I received an opportunity such as this to express my creativity. My experiences at Starbot have allowed me to apply everything I have learned in the last 15 years of my life into a positive creation: A robot. I've become a slave of the bot!"

— Jesus Romero, student

"A large percentage of today's youth in America are wasting their time staying at home and lying around, doing drugs, participating in gangs or worse. Robotics keeps kids busy, and lets them do something in which they excel. This past year has been my first year participating in FIRST

Their brains are kicking into high gear: Nola Garcia and David Kirkpatrick explain new motor mounts to Judith Martinez, Yvonne Feliciano, Sergio Sanchez, Paul Grata, Adriana Bermudez, and Danny Espinosa
Photo Courtesy Starbot/ Photo by Bill Garcia

(For Inspiration and Recognition of Science and Technology) Robotics. We won our division and we ended up as National Semi-Finalists. Building a robot takes a lot of time and dedication, but it is well worth it. To see something that you have spent countless of hours working on come to life is one of the most amazing feelings ever—no words can ever begin to describe it. Having robotics in my life has been a worthwhile experience, and will continue to be for decades to come."

— **Adriana Bermudez**

"Being in a robotics program has been one of the of the greatest experiences of my life. It has enabled me to use my imagination along with my math and science skills to create an extraordinary machine. I learned the importance of the team work and commitment, though the best thing has been the tons of fun we have in a safe learning environment."

— **Judith Martinez, student**

"I have learned so many things ahead of my time. Building a robot really has exercised my mind and has made me able to see more solutions for more problems. I have learned discipline as well. It takes hard work and determination, and you have to stay on task. But most important, it has been lots of fun, and your reward is seeing lifeless materials come to life."

— **Danny Espinosa, student**

"Being involved with building robots has allowed me to use my knowledge of math and physics to solve a real world problem. I have been able to grow mentally and socially because of it. Upon entering college I know that I will have a great advantage over those that have not had the same opportunity as me, and the same goes for when I begin searching for a job. If I could change one thing, it would be to have joined much earlier in my high school years. Nothing can compare to the feeling of watching your lifeless creation made of aluminum and steel slowly come to life for the first time."

— **Sergio Sanchez, student**

"I am blessed to be surrounded by an incredible group of young people that have given back to me their teacher an abundance of knowledge and experience in the area of robotics. The student-teacher roles have reversed and now I am their pupil. This is the hobby that I never had growing up, and now has given me an avenue to express the creative side of myself. The sheer excitement and motivation that it gives me cannot be expressed in simple words."

— **Coach David Kirkpatrick**

FIRST Robotics

Many robot combat competitors (including Michael and Nola) have been involved with FIRST Robotics, a program that challenges teams consisting mostly of teens to build bots with specific parts and tasks in mind. These robots aren't meant to fight; they're designed by the teams to perform specific assignments. The program is demanding, in terms of both time and brain power. "You would think that grades would go down because of the commitment involved," says Nola, "but instead they go up." FIRST is a great way to learn first-hand with seasoned builders—teams have been coached by the likes of Team Nightmare's Jim Smentowski and Team BioHazard's Carlo Bertocchini (read Carlo's account of a FIRST competition at the end of the next chapter).

BattleBots® IQ

Robot combat programs for schools are in the works too. BattleBots® is piloting a high school robotic curriculum this year with 25 teachers, under the leadership of bot builders Nola Garcia, and Michael Bastoni, with MIT professor Alex Slocum. "The BattleBots® IQ curriculum is being built as an online book, and it's being done by students, for students," explains Michael. "The rate at which these students can process and use technology and information is astounding. The program doesn't simply change kids; it gives them a place that validates who they are. All of a sudden it's cool to be smart." Expansion is to be expected, given the overwhelming initial response to the program: "I have a list of 800 people who have e-mailed me from the U.S., Canada, the U.K., and from as far away as Nigeria," Nola reports.

Bot Bash lives up to its name: Evil Fish Tank and Gator thrashing around the arena
Photo courtesy Bot Bash LLC/ Photo by John Kittelsrud

Regional **events**

When it comes to robot competitions, there's a time and a place for pretty much everything. "If you're interested in underwater robots, there's a competition for you," observes Team BioHazard's Carlo Bertocchini. "There are competitions for flying robots, micromouse mazes where the bot has to get through a maze, and robot hockey too. Firefighting robot competitions are some of the most popular amateur competitions. Bot Bash® is also good, which is a tournament down in Arizona that offers some very memorable matches with small to medium-sized robots." Want to see something really bizarre? We're willing to bet there's a robot competition out there that will exceed your expectations—just check out our resources section and www.robotbooks.com for updates of the new and weird competitions that are springing up all the time.

Behind the Lexan®

If you're anything like most bot buffs, you're happiest when you're behind that Lexan® barrier in an arena, yelling like there's no tomorrow. "Audience sentiment definitely plays a big role in robot combat," notes builder and longtime fan

Whole lotta fist-shakin' going on: The BattleBots® crowd
Photo courtesy BattleBots, Inc.®/ Photo by Daniel Longmire

Dave Thau. "If everybody's booing you, it's not very much fun to win. So builders try not to take out the other robot right away, and know not to beat a bot when it's down." A competitor may make the critical choice to help his/her opponent out from under the spikes and risk losing—all for the sake of a good show. Robot Action League member and good sport Lisa Winter cautions the crowd to use their power wisely. "Don't boo the bots that don't work," she urges. "Fans should know that all these people really worked hard and tried to make a good bot." "People actually yell, 'We hate you!' I can see cheering for your favorite, but really hating the other robot isn't very sporting," agrees BioHazard's Carlo Bertocchini. "Still, it doesn't bother me too much—in fact, I'm glad they get emotionally involved with the robots. I mean, the worst possible thing a match could be would be boring."

Loud as they wanna be

Arena competitions aren't exactly like what you see on TV. For starters, they're *much* louder. The robots make their unholy din, and the fans make theirs. "We just returned from Robot Wars® in England, and the fans there seem to root for the destruction of any and all of the competitors in a unified and rather bloodthirsty manner. Competing in an arena surrounded by 2000 of these fans shouting and chanting is quite an experience," says Mark Joerger. "The noise level was comparable to an NBA playoff game! They cheered hardest for bots with surprising design features, superior driving, and clever attacks and escapes." Team Robot Widow's Gillian Blood confirms this account of U.K. fans: "Robot combat fans are usually pretty mad people, actually. Roboteering seems to provoke interest in people from all ages and all walks of life. It seems to have created a cult following." Inertia Labs' Reason Bradley reports a similar age range, decibel level, and fervor among U.S. BattleBots® fans too. "It's a pretty amazing cross-section of people who show up: young and old, both genders, a whole range of backgrounds. Technical people are into it, but so are people who are into smashing stuff. During a match, *everyone's* screaming. It's great when you hear them chanting for you. The Toro fans blew my mind—I have no idea who those guys with TORO written on their chests were!"

Onto something big

Arena tournaments are also far bigger than you might guess from TV. "At the last BattleBots® competition there were five days of fighting with almost eight hours of matches a day, but you only get to see a few of the matches on the TV show," explains Team Ziggo's Jonathan Ridder. To get a better sense of the range of the bots being built, bot builder and fan Dave Thau recommends going to BattleBots® competitions in the first few days, when preliminary rounds are held. "Preliminaries have lots of unusual cute robots," he says. "It's not like other professional sporting events like the Americas Cup, where all those boats have become so similar. Plus there are mostly builders in the audience at preliminaries, so you get to talk to them." More teenagers are beginning to show up at preliminaries, and many with robots in tow. "I think there are so many 14- and 15-year olds interested in robots because when BattleBots® first aired on Comedy Central, it showed right after *South Park*," says BioHazard's Carlo Bertocchini. "So that was the demographic at the time. Now some of these kids are developing incredible robot building skills." What happens if *all* the people who get inspired at preliminaries show up with robots next time? Step right up, says BattleBots® co-founder Greg Munson. "BattleBots® is open to everybody—we're interested in robots, not resumes."

Try? There is no try. There is only do or not do.
— Yoda

Taking the leap

At some point in every robot fan's mind, this thought appears: "I bet I could do that!" To which we say: There's only one way to find out. Seriously—give us one good reason why you couldn't compete. Robot combat is the one sport in which any truly motivated individual could compete: your gender, age, size, physical abilities, popularity, looks and GPA

The South Bay RoboWarriors conspire over their bot, Mauler 5150
Photo courtesy BattleBots, Inc.®/ Photo by Daniel Longmire

are irrelevant in the arena. "Pretty much anyone can get out there and build a perfectly competitive robot," says Robotica® champ Mark Joerger. "It really isn't rocket science." Robot combat is different from other sports when it comes to audience participation, as Team BioHazard's Carlo Bertocchini points out. "The majority of televised sports are off limits for most people; they are strictly spectators," he says. "People watch wrestling, but the average person could not possibly compete in that—they couldn't be that huge. But a lot of people think of themselves as tinkerers, and have mechanical skills. I'm not saying it's easy, but it's theoretically possible for a good percentage of the people in America and across the world to put a robot together and compete."

Up close
and personal

Once you've made up your mind to compete, you'll realize that you're in good company. Scratch that: *extremely* good company. When asked what the best thing about competing is, every champion builder says the same thing: The people. "You know when you're friends with a person for a long time, you kind of

Bot bonding: Christian Carlberg and Jason Bardis prepare Mini Inferno to run The Gauntlet at Robotica®
Photo courtesy The Learning Channel, Inc.

start thinking of exactly the same things at the same time, and you know exactly what they're going to say next? Well, many times I meet other builders for the first time and it feels like just like that!" explains bot builder Ilya Polyakov. "The pits are a wonderful community where like-minded people get to share and talk about the very thing that makes people roll their eyes the other 350 days out of the year," jokes Jason Bardis. Builders do their utmost to maintain this sense of congeniality, even now that arena events have reached colossal proportions. "I've never been to such a large event where you have so much in common with so many people," says Team Vladiator's Gage Cauchois. "The only tragedy is that with maybe 2,000 competitors, you don't really get much of a chance to know people."

Rules for **the ruthless**

With so many builders participating in robot competitions, how do they maintain their sense of community? Simple. Just as the Knights of the Round Table had their code of chivalry at jousting matches, robot builders have an unspoken code of conduct in the arena that dates back to the early days of the sport. Sure, builders are ruthless with their robots in the arena—but that's no cause for bad blood among builders. "When those two robots are in the ring, you want to win," says Nola Garcia of Team Fembot and Team Loki. "But as soon as the doors to the BattleBox™ open, the builders will do anything for each other. It's very rare to find someone who isn't into the spirit of the sport. I'm not sure that always translates to TV." New builders pick up code cues from their peers in the pits, and newbies who are quick studies of this code soon find themselves respected as cluebies.

R-E-S-P-E-C-T

Mutual respect and humility have always been the name of the game in robot combat; champions don't gloat, and the trophy-less take their losses in stride. As longtime veteran Jim Smentowski of Team Nightmare says, "This isn't the World Wrestling Federation; being cocky just doesn't cut it. There's really no place for that in the sport."

Robotica® champ Mark Joerger agrees. "If you're pleasant and show reasonable humility, the other builders will go out of their way to help you out if you get into a jam. On the other hand, if you show up and behave like an ass, you're gonna find the pits a lonely place." There's no dishonor in losing—only in dealing with it dishonorably. "I've heard one or two people mumble something about sabotage or the judges in the heat of the moment, but they were always embarrassed about it afterwards," says Christian Carlberg of Team Coolrobots. As Team Sinister's Mark Setrakian points out, all those who show up with a robot have already proved themselves worthy of admiration. "I admire all the robots. Just that the builders went for it, and managed to show up with something—let alone something that works—gets my respect," he says. "I hope they all stick with it."

Help out

In robot combat, it's nearly impossible to get by without a little help from your friends. And as the maxim goes, you've got to give to receive. "People are super cool about giving and lending stuff. I mean at Nascar, you don't see people come up to their competitors and say, 'Here's an engine,'" notes Inertia Labs' Reason Bradley. "The second year we competed at Robot Wars®, we lost our speed controller. Trey [Roski, BattleBots® co-founder] comes along and says, 'Here!' and shoves us his $1000 speed controller across the table. We were slated to up against him, and asked him if he realized this. He was like, 'Yeah, I know.'" Such good deeds are often returned, and seldom forgotten. "I remember one time Dan Danknick brought us some lunch in the pits, and it made a big difference in how the day's matches went for us," recalls Mark Setrakian of Team Sinister. "Sometimes you don't have right tools, sometimes you forget to bring food—but everybody pulls together. We all have enough in common that we get along well, and we all try to be as helpful as we can to everyone who asks."

Laugh it **off**

Victory lap: Aaron Maxwell Joerger rides Robotica® champion Run Amok
Photo courtesy The Learning Channel, Inc.

With its rise in popularity, robot combat *is* getting to be serious business—but builders still know how to have a good time. Team Díotóir's Pete Redmond is all for poking fun at the competition, as long as no one gets hurt. "We may wear silly hats and furry coats to competitions, but at least we don't dress in women's clothes like Vinny Blood [of Razer fame]. I mean there's having a laugh and there's making a statement," wisecracks Pete. In this sport, a good sense of humor is a critical part of the game. "At the BattleBots® season 3.0 tournament, Reason [Bradley, of Inertia Labs] knew I was having hard time getting technical clearance," says Team Vladiator's Gage Cauchois. "So he comes over with this dead serious expression and says, 'They want to see you in the office, man.' My heart stopped. Then I realized he was joking. That was a good one! I really appreciate the sense of humor people have in the pits. You've got to have sense of humor to subject yourself to the BattleBox™." No matter how much time, money and soul has been put into a bot's design, there's a good chance you will be scraping it up off the arena floor in pieces. "If your bot gets turned into steel wool, you just laugh, shake your opponent's hand, and go off to build a new bot that will do the same to them the next time you cross paths," says Run Amok builder Mark Joerger.

The creation of something new is not accomplished by the intellect, but by the play instinct acting from inner necessity. The creative mind plays with the objects it loves.
— Carl Jung

BOT SHOT

Jim Smentowski: Robotcombat.com founder/bot builder

Web site: robotcombat.com

Team Nightmare

Robot credits:
Nightmare (HW)
Backlash (LW)
Whirligig (LW)
Junior (MW)
Hercules (HW)
Locust (SHW)

Home base: Rohnert Park, California

Born: 1969

Domo arigato, Mr. Roboto

After going to my first robot combat competition in 1996, I was hooked. I knew I had to build my own bot. I had no idea what I was doing—I'd never even cut a piece of metal or taken shop class in school. I spent a lot of time researching on the Internet and at the local library, and asked the other competitors lots of questions about the basics. My first robot Hercules was ready for battle in less than a year. Now almost five years later, robot combat is practically a full-time job for me. It's an obsession. I entered *four* bots in the BattleBots®, season 3.0 competition. It was pretty crazy. I sponsored 14-year-old Jeremy Franklin to drive Whirligig (my second lightweight), since you can't have two entries in the same weight class. I was a coach at the US FIRST robot competition in 1999 and was really happy with the way Jeremy drove the team robot. He was only 12 at the time.

Kicking back

At the 1999 Long Beach BattleBots® competition they had a thin layer of plastic over the top of the BattleBox™. There were openings in it and things were flying through the gaps. For safety reasons, they asked me if there was some way I could reduce the speed or effectiveness of Nightmare's spinning disc, so I reversed the polarity of the motor and spun it the other direction. That did the trick, but it totally went against the design objective. Spinning upward, Nightmare's disc kicks the other robots up and away. Spinning downward, it instead kicks my robot backwards. I went in there and tossed myself six-feet in the air, just for fun. The crowd loved it.

A real eye-opener

In robot combat safety is a big concern. Luckily, I've still got all my fingers, but every one of my bots gets a little bit of blood on it. Once, when I went in for my annual eye exam, my optometrist looked at my contacts and was like, "Did you know that you've got a little piece of metal embedded in one of your lenses?" It was actually rusting in there. If I hadn't been wearing contacts that piece of metal would be in my eye. So now I ALWAYS wear my goggles. Every builder should.

Jim with Backlash
Photo courtesy Battle Bots, Inc.®/Photo by David Longmire

That's about the size of it

Nightmare is a pretty visual robot. I think he's the biggest heavyweight out there right now at six-and-a-half-feet long and four-feet tall. Size wise, he's bigger than some of the super heavyweights. He's a monster. I used to take him down to the end of this abandoned road with a big 50-gallon steel drum and hit that a few times. There was an overpass so if anything flew too high, it would hit the underside of the freeway. Nightmare could actually throw the drum about 10 feet in the air! He's a lot more powerful now than in those early days, too powerful not to have the type of protection you get from an enclosed arena so I don't really test drive his weapon anymore.

BOT SHOT

Mark Joerger: father/bot builder

Web site: www.open.org/~joerger/

Team Run Amok: Aaron Max Joerger and
Lissa Joerger, teammates

Robot credits:
Run Amok (Robotica® champion, 2001)
Run Away (Robot Wars® Tag Team Finalist, 2001)

Home base: Salem, Oregon

Born: 1952

Knee-high sci-fi

I grew up in the 50s and early 60s and watched a lot of bad science-fiction movies with evil robots that I thought were really frightening and really cool. I suppose the first robot I saw may have been Robby the Robot from *Forbidden Planet*. I started building "robots" out of cardboard boxes and tin foil to decorate my childhood bedroom. I can remember a few that I built with my Erector set. Young boys build robots with LEGOS® now, but it's all the same idea.

Like father, like son

I've tried to involve my son (Aaron Max, age 10) in whatever projects I've been working on since he was tall enough to see what was on my workbench. We have had some small competition successes in the past, slot racing and building a gravity racer out of vegetables. One night after an episode of *Junkyard Wars*, a notice came on about an upcoming robot challenge on the Learning Channel. Aaron Max had become an even bigger fan of robot combat than I was. He could name every bot from the BattleBots® tournaments, who built them, who they had fought against, and what their strengths and weaknesses were. I had a notebook full of designs that I was going to get to—someday. This looked like a perfect father/son project.

Mark Joerger and Aaron Maxwell Joerger, Robotica® champions
Photo courtesy The Learning Channel, Inc.

And ... action!

Robotica® was our first robot competition. The event took place over four very long days at the old ABC studios in Hollywood. The *General Hospital* soap opera films on a nearby sound stage, and it was a little odd to wheel your robot past a TV set. I actually tried to use a pay phone near the robot storage impound before I realized it was a prop. The best thing about Robotica® was that the competition was more than a test of brute fighting power. The bots were tested in a variety of ways which, as a builder, I found very rewarding. The contestants weren't lost in a sea of other competitors—there were only about 30 teams. I made some very good friends there.

On a bot buzz

We had seven weeks from the time the Robotica® rules were released until we had to ship Run Amok off to LA. In those seven weeks, I lost 15 pounds and couldn't sleep nights as my head was abuzz with ideas and wild concepts. Winning Robotica® was a gigantic thrill that I hope all aspiring robot builders can equal some day. I was so exhausted by the end of the competition that afterwards I had to ask my wife, "Who won Robotica®?" She assured me that, in fact, we had won. It became easier to accept after the engraved trophy arrived, and after I got to see the show on TLC a few weeks later.

131

BOT SHOT

Christian Carlberg: bot builder

Web site: www.coolrobots.com

Team Coolrobots: with Brian Roe and Luke Khanlian

Robot credits:
    Buzzcut (LW)
    Pretty Hate Machine (MW)
    Little Slice of Hell (SHW)
    L'il Plumber (LW)
    Nasty (HW)
    Dreadnought (SHW) (with Brian Roe, Luke Khanlian
        and Mike Ballard)
    Little Slice (LW)
    Toe Crusher (LW)—2nd Place BotBash, 1999
    Knee Breaker (MW) (with Clint Lynch and Luke Khanlian);
        2nd Place BattleBots®, 1999
    Slugger (HW) (with Jason Bardis)
    Minion (SHW) (with Brian Roe and Luke Khanlian)—Super
        Heavyweight Champion BattleBots®, 1999, 2000; Super
        Heavyweight Runner-Up BattleBots®, 2001; Super
        Heavyweight Rumble Winner Battlebots®, 2000
    Overkill (HW) (with Frank and Mike Ballard)

Home base: North Hills, California

Born: 1970

Earning his place in the pits

I sneaked into the pits at the 1995 Robot Wars® event, and came away saying, "That's it. I'm going to compete next year." I didn't get my robot done in time for the 1996 competition—classic first-time builder's syndrome—but I sneaked into the pits again and started planning two walking robots for 1997. I got them done, and they did OK, not great, in competition. But I realized I was onto something when Mark Setrakian came over and said, "I really like your robot." That was a defining moment for me, to have this guy who builds incredible robots like The Master compliment my robot.

From battle-field to Disneyland

Cool Robots started to take off after the 1997 Robot Wars®. We were the first team to bring successful walking robots to competition, and we won the first time we entered a robot in BattleBots® super-heavyweight division. We got written up in *Wired* in 1998, which led to a job offer from Walt Disney Imagineering. I did LED, smoke and fire effects for Tokyo Disney, and still work as a consultant for Disney. I now have my own company, C2 Robots, and I'm pleased to say we just finished developing a robot that cleans water pollution. It's been kind of unbeliev-

Christian with Minion
Photo courtesy BattleBots, Inc.®/ Photo by Daniel Longmire

able, really—I've only been building robots for six years. There's probably not an engineer alive that hasn't dreamed of building fighting robots, working for Disney, or inventing technology that makes a difference in people's lives—and here I get to do all three.

Beating the clock

People think that robot combat is about competing against other robot builders, but it's really about competing against time. When you're just starting out, you might miss out on one or two competitions because you can't get your robot built in time. On *www.coolrobots.com*, I give a lot of tips to help new builders leapfrog over those mistakes I learned about the hard way. The trick is to learn your lessons early on, so you're not making those mistakes when it's down to the wire and the competition is tomorrow. It takes a lot of time and effort just to get a robot ready to fight for three minutes. Are those three minutes in the arena worth it? Absolutely. When you see winners jumping up and down, it's not because they beat the competition—it's because they get to fight again.

BOT SHOT

Ilya Polyakov: college student/bot builder

Web site: www.teamcarnivore.com

Team Carnivore: Mike Mass, Ben Larue, Lev Ioffe, and
Lenny Jacinto, teammates

Robot credits:
Carnivore (MW)
Carnivore, Jr.
Hexafobia, Jr.
Blade Runner (MW)
Flame Boat (Airboat with flame-thrower)

Home base: New York, New York

Born: 1979 (Moscow, Russia)

A young pyromaniac makes good

The first time I remember being interested in robots was in the 10th
grade. My hobbies were [computer] hacking and model helicopters. I
got really sick of building things out of kits, such as RC helicopters and
planes. For a while I turned to special effects, but then I thought, "Why
mimic sci-fi when you can make it a reality?" I started to build things
like boats with flame-throwers and the like, and then I discovered
robot combat. The second I saw two bots fighting on the Discovery
Channel, in 1995, I knew I had to do this. I started pulling random parts
together and got a bot [Carnivore] built in about five months. The thing
started smoking and almost caught fire about two minutes before my
first match.

State of the art

As my latest bot's name implies, I'm a huge *Blade Runner* fan. Syd Mead's
outlook on the future totally inspired me. The general look of my robot
was largely motivated by that movie. I also like art by H.R. Geiger and
think Survival Research Labs is awesome. SRL was the main inspiration
for my earlier projects. Music is also important to me—German mini-
mal house techno really describes my bot: fast, simple and hard-hitting.

Jack-of-all-trades

For me robot combat is definitely a creative outlet. I express myself through designing and building my robots. That is one of the most wonderful things about the sport, you get to experience everything from art to math, and more. It's been a crash course in everything from marketing to media, and from business to teambuilding. I also learned a whole bunch about wood working and home improvement. I had to build a shop from scratch in an unfinished basement at my parents' house. This required me to construct everything from the walls to the plumbing—totally not something you'd expect to come out of robot combat! When I make composite parts for robots, 90% of the work is spent making the wooden molds. That means I have to carve them and then spend hours finishing the surface. In the last year, my shop floor saw way more wood chips than steel ones.

Ilya with Blade Runner
Photo Courtesy Team Carnivore

Great minds think alike

One of the best things about robot combat is seeing your ideas turn from a scribbled sketch to a real machine. Being able to see this thing you built face-off against something another person built, and having thousands of people there to share it with you is equally amazing. Meeting the other builders is also a huge part of the experience. No matter their age or background, we are all alike. Sometimes I seriously think we're all related or something. It's the only place on the planet where I feel like I really fit in. You know when you're friends with a person for a long time and you kind of start thinking exactly the same things at the same time? Well, many times when I meet other builders it feels like just like that.

BOT SHOT

Donald Hutson: mad scientist/bot builder

Web site: www.mutantrobots.com

Team Mutant Robots: Dawn Bernstein, David Cook, David Bleakly and Mike Moore, teammates

Robot credits:
Tazbot (HW) 2000 Rumble Champ
Diesector (SHW) 2000 Duel Champ
Skywalker (Walking robot) Prototype

Home base: San Diego, California

Born: 1968

Sucked into the vortex

The first time I saw robot combat on TV in 1995, I knew I was watching the birth of a truly unique sporting event. Within three weeks, I constructed the turret for Tazbot and had the basic design principle worked out on paper. One month later I was testing Tazbot and making hotel reservations for the upcoming event in San Francisco. The opportunity to create your own robot and send it into battle is very exciting! Some of my design inspiration comes from classic robot toys and science fiction movies, but most is from builders like Mark Setrakian, Christian Carlberg and many others who build robots not only to win, but for the art of mechanical engineering and just for the sake of building a cool bot. If after four to five months of hardcore building, your robot works and passes safety you have already won the battle! If the bot wins one fight or proves to be a champion, it's just that much sweeter.

Action hero

Mutant robots are built to fight the good old fashion way—gladiator style! The interchangeable weapons on both Tazbot and Diesector were designed mainly as self-righting tools and to gain control of other robots. I tried to make sure that the weapons were capable of inflicting damage from any angle. The main strength of both these robots is

Donald with Tazbot
Photo courtesy BattleBots, Inc.®/ Photo by Daniel Longmire

speed, agility and most of all, strategy. I think my robots are kind of
unique and have a lot of character, which seems to make them favorites
with the crowd. But all the bots are unique in their own way. Some
robots may look kind of similar but it's the mechanical workings and the
heart of the robot that counts.

It's alive!

I work as an engineer on a robotic platform know as "Nomad" for the
Neuroscience Institute in San Diego, California
(http://www.nsi.edu/nomad/). Nomad is a brain based robotic platform
that is not quite a computer or a robot. Instead, it is a machine that actually thinks and makes mistakes. Nomad is connected wirelessly to a mul-
titude of high-powered computers to simulate the neurons in our brains.
Nomad learns by developing associations between his given senses and
his environment. Battle bots are rigid warriors built for fun; the robots I
build at work are purely for science.

chapter 5

Bot Boot Camp

Whatever you can do, or dream you can, begin it.
Boldness has genius, power and magic in it.
— Goethe

Scheming

Most people daydream, but not bot builders: They scheme.
Daydreamers are content to muse and wonder, but bot builders investigate and plot. They're not necessarily more devious than anyone else (though some can be quite cagey about their control systems). It's just that their brains just don't have an off switch. Their minds are always racing ahead of the competition, collecting data and working out a winning approach. So intelligence gathering, design, and testing are not just compulsory first steps in building a robot—they're consuming passions.

Real knowledge is to know the extent
of one's ignorance.
— Confucius

Not-so-artificial
intelligence

Good news! You already possess the one crucial bit of intelligence you need to build a successful robot. This is the information that will save you hundreds, if not thousands of hours in build time: The wheel has already been invented. And so have motors, and hydraulics, and pneumatics, and almost everything else you might want to build into your bot. So don't go thinking you have to concoct everything from scratch without a recipe. There are more builders' cookbooks out there on the Web than you imagine—you just need to log on and start sleuthing.

Lurk before you leap

Start with the Web sites in our Resources section, but don't stop there. "Read absolutely everything that the successful builders have written on Web sites and discussion

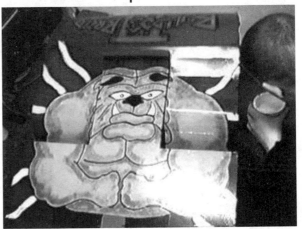

A man's best friend, a robot's worst enemy: Bulldog II
Photo courtesy Tony Somerfield/Photo by Tony Somerfield

groups," advises Robotica® champion Mark Joerger. "Most builders are very generous with their knowledge and you can learn a great deal from their experience. After you have read up on the subject, you can write to specific builders with specific questions—but please read the information on their website first, and ask specific questions. Do not write to a builder and ask, 'I want to build a robot—how do I do that?' " Bulldog builder Tony Somerville agrees: "Visit every robot Web site you can access to pick up tips before you fix your mind on a design."

Small talk, big ideas

Once you've read everything you can get your hands (or cursor) on, you should fill in the gaps in your knowledge by hanging out with fellow robot builders. "Join a local club or travel to a robotics club meeting," recommends sumo bot builder Dion Brewington. "You'll find that anybody in the field is ecstatic that someone new is showing interest in the hobby, and we all love to brag about our robots' features. This gives you a good opportunity to see other designs up close and discuss why they didn't pursue alternate designs. Get information on your design ideas from others who are knowledgeable in the field. Sometimes it's that small talk that saves you from project failure later."

Know your obstacles

Robot Wars® arena shot
Photo courtesy Mentorn Barraclough Carey Ltd.

Talking with the experts will help you decide whether you're going to design your robot with a specific competition in mind. In addition to strict weight limitations, each competition offers specific technical challenges that you'll need to consider: sumo robot competitions admit no weapons, BattleBots® has killsaws in the floor, Robot Wars® features flame pits, and Robotica® tests speed and maneuverability in addition to fighting capabilities.

Competitive bot builders study arena challenges carefully before pursuing a design. Homework helped Pete Redmond design Díotóir to be a successful Robot Wars® competitor. "The pit in Robot Wars® is more of a problem for fast robots, so I designed Díotóir for torque rather than speed," he explains. "Díotóir is not really fast enough to accidentally drive into the pit, but usually is strong enough to push others in to it."

One design
doesn't fit all

Run Amok masters the Robotica®, maze
Photo courtesy The Learning Channel, Inc

If you're seeking that one robot design that can conquer all bot competitions, Robotica® champ Mark Joerger warns, you may be out of luck. "I think a number of the other teams built bots with which they intended to go on to other robot competitions, or were unduly influenced by the designs that they had seen in such battle-centered contests. I carefully examined the challenges of the courses laid out for Robotica®. Our design was simple, rugged, used proven components, and was easy to repair and maintain. I wanted something that I would be comfortable with driving, and made an early decision to go with an automotive steering system where the front wheels actually turn to steer the vehicle. For the sake of simplicity, I also wanted a single drive-motor. After I examined a number of design alternatives and rejected them, I stumbled across a Web site from a guy in Florida who had built a couple of remote controlled lawn mowers. The mowers were simple, tough, and nimble—just the concept I needed for Run Amok."

Proven ideas—**with** a twist

Savvy builders like Mark borrow concepts and information from a number of sources, adding an element of the unexpected to keep the competition guessing. "Suss out potential competition, read the tips on the robot building sites and get as many ideas as you can from experienced roboteers—then change them about a bit and make them your own," says Fiona Mason, member of Team Robot Widows and designer of the unique spiked rolling pin weapon on Widow's Revenge. Team Fembot's Nola Garcia agrees: "Honor what's been done before,

Kiss the competition goodbye: Widow's Revenge
Photo courtesy Team Robot Widows/ Photo by E. Cathcart

but also ask: Is there another way to do that? Preparation is important, but you should always look for solutions that haven't been found yet."

Scaling the evolutionary ladder

If you go into the design phase equipped with both background knowledge and your imagination, you'll be doing yourself a favor—and the sport too. "People are doing their research on robot-building, as you can see from all the impressive new robots out there," says Christian Carlberg, Minion builder and founder of www.coolrobots.com. "That evolution is what makes the sport exciting. Everyone has different ideas about the perfect robot—and the more of those ideas that make it to the arena, the more interesting it is for everyone."

Great things are not done by impulse, but by a series of small things brought together.
— Vincent Van Gogh

Design

Now that you've gathered intelligence on robot building, you're privy to the secret of breakthrough robot design: You won't find it in a kit. Kits are great for fun and practice, but you can do better. The very best robot you can possibly build is the one that's lodged in your brain and refuses to vacate the premises.

Learn to KISS

Don't expect your genius to be realized overnight. You should be prepared to simplify your design and/or build a very simple robot first. "Most people have to get through that first robot to learn most of the skills they need," explains BioHazard builder Carlo Bertocchini. "Then the next time around, you can get a little bolder." If you have the good fortune to join a team of more experienced robot builders, you'll notice they never forget to KISS: Keep It Simple, Stupid. "Work with no more than one new technology at a time," recommends Mark Joerger of Team Run Amok. "You aren't gonna win anything with a machine that exceeds your capacity to build, drive, and maintain—it will only add to your stress level at the event." Bear in mind also that your robot must be easy to repair, says Team Loki and Team Fembot leader Nola Garcia: "There has to be enough room inside the bot so that you can work on it in between matches. The more bells and whistles you add, the harder it can be to fix—and sometimes you only get 20 minutes for repairs."

Simple genius

As you gain skills and streamline your approach, you should be steadily working toward your design inspiration. "You can't do something that's

Wokking all over the competition: Blendo
Photo courtesy BattleBots, Inc.®/ Photo by Daniel Longmire

so far beyond your abilities that your reach exceeds your grasp," cautions Robot Wars® creator Marc Thorpe." But in terms of a concept, it needs to be something that you're really passionate about—because passion is the fuel that's necessary to see you through the long process of making the thing work." Ingenuity and simplicity don't have to be at odds; Team Blendo revolutionized the sport when they came in with a bot made from a wok that harnessed the power of momentum. "Try to think of something that's never been done just for an interesting effect, and you may be the one to evolve the sport," says Armored Robotics' Rik Winter. "But at the same time, keep it simple."

Strategic uses for
cocktail napkins

Once you've got a robot in mind that suits your skills and ignites your imagination, you need to get that concept out of your head and into a sketch. Sure, a lot of builders use software programs to make 3D renderings—Team Deadblow's Grant Imahara uses AutoCAD, and the Infernolab's Jason Bardis uses ProEngineer—but you don't have to be that fancy. The back of a cocktail napkin (well, maybe a few of them) could work for starters. The important part is not whether you begin with

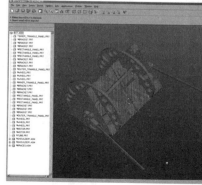

Towering Inferno in theory
Pro/Engineer rendering courtesy Jason Bardis/ Image by Jason Bardis

Towering Inferno in practice
Photo courtesy Jason Bardis/Photo by Jason Bardis

elaborate diagram, but whether you begin with a strategic approach. "You've got to make plans and envision it," says Reactor's Michael Bastoni. "Otherwise, it usually doesn't get made. It's just too complicated to wing it."

Assumptions **are the** enemy

While you're sketching out your design, you should be refining your approach. "Good design is not about assumptions," explains Michael Bastoni. "You test. You've got

Team PTNA's Brandon Gunn, Erik DeGiorgi and Ron Partridge confer on design parameters
Photo courtesy of Michael Bastoni/Photo by Tamson Burgess

to think about what the robot is supposed to do and be." Even the most basic designs require careful strategy. "Simple is anything but simple," says Marc Thorpe, creator of Robot Wars®. "There's so much to learn and know about what has to work, which is fundamentally different from things that you want to look good. If something looks good or doesn't, that's subjective—whether something works isn't. If your robot only sort of works, that's the same as not working." To make sure you've covered all strategic design considerations, check out the design overview provided by Team Saber (builders of Fusion and Endotherm) at www.teamsaber.com/tutorial/design.html.

Tough questions, **tougher robot**

Brutal honesty at the design stage is critical; overestimating your robot early on can prove fatal in a fight. "When you're designing a robot you use the same the tools that you do when you're designing your life," says Michael Bastoni of Reactor fame. "You ask yourself, 'What are my strengths, what are my weaknesses?' " Armor shouldn't be an afterthought: your rubber duckie design may have a vicious flipping bill, but there had better be some serious metal under that cheery yellow exterior to protect the inner workings of your robot. "If there's a big enough hole in your armor, the other bot will find it," says the voice of Reason Bradley of Inertia Labs. Be realistic about your weapon, too, cautions Reason: "The most common misconception is thinking 'Let's use this saw that could cut a human being right in half.' Well, maybe it could cut a person right in half—but when you're running into a garbage can, it's not going to do much. It may only make a dent before it breaks the saw. Make sure you build the robot around your weapon." And don't forget that robots like Toro are out to flip you—make sure you have low ground clearance and preferably a self-righting mechanism.

Get a **move** on

Maneuverability is another key design consideration. As most builders will tell you, driving is often the deciding factor in a match—so complicated control electronics and other design features that might cause drivers performance anxiety should be reconsidered. "I'd recommend going with a design that gives you

Rik Winter's KMM: In design
Image courtesy of Rik Winter/CAD rendering by Rik Winter

Rik Winter's KMM: In reality
Photo courtesy of Rik Winter/Photo by
Rik Winter

more control," says Team Coolrobots' Christian Carlberg. "Go with four-wheeled robots instead of two-wheeled ones. I think in future competitions we'll see better electronics and better controls—anything that makes the driving better and the robot more maneuverable." Rik Winter warns that computer-aided steering systems and sensors may not be able to outwit an agile human foe: "I'm a software engineer, and still I always tell people: Do not go down that path. There's nothing quicker or more strategic than a human with good hand-eye coordination."

When push comes to shove

Taking control of a match is not just about maneuvering your own robot—you need to be able to maneuver your opponent's robot too. "Torque, not speed, is important," says Lisa Winter. "Speed looks good on camera but it doesn't necessarily help you win. You want to be able to push people around—and for that you need force and torque." Hydraulic and pneumatic power sources tend to deliver the highest torque, but they are extremely difficult and dangerous and not recommended for novices. "Don't try to get into tracks or pneumatics or hydraulics or other big weapons," suggests Jason Bardis. "Start simple and small, maybe a drive wedge or ramming box with spikes."

Power to the people

Instead of hankering after hydraulics, invest some time researching what combination of motors, controllers, and batteries will deliver the highest power/pocketbook ratio for your specific design needs. Available technologies and prices are changing all the time, so you'll need to do some research on this one. You can find answers to your burning motor questions, learn how not to blow up your Vantec speed controller, and comparison shop for batteries at www.robotbooks.com.

Anticipate the worst,
and be pleasantly surprised

Once you have several napkin sketches that take into consideration weaponry, defense, maneuverability, and power, you'll be raring to fire up the blowtorch—but for bot's sake, don't. First, map out your design in detail. "Before you make a single part, have the whole thing planned out down to the last screw," says Blade Runner builder Ilya Polyakov. "Follow Murphy's Law religiously. If you think something might break, it definitely will. If you think a part will not get hit, it will. Even if you're pretty sure something will not break, it still might." Reason Bradley concurs: "Design your entire robot first, down to every wire, every bolt."

What's with these guys? Are they gluttons for punishment? Quite the contrary. Seasoned builders know that brains beat bravado in the arena. Create a strategic blueprint that is as practical as it is ambitious, and you may save yourself the agony of defeat. "That fancy weapon system isn't going to have a chance to destroy the opposition if your drive train breaks down and leaves you stranded in the middle of the arena," says Robotica® winner Mark Joerger.

Blueprints that
are neither

So you need a blueprint—but no one says it has to be blue, or a print. If you're a quick study with software, you could build one in Pro Engineer or AutoCAD. But Grant Imahara didn't stop at AutoCAD design: he built an amazing full-scale prototype of Deadblow in clear acrylic that

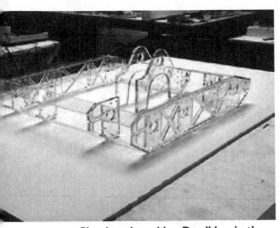

Clearly a clever idea: Deadblow in the making
Photo courtesy Grant Imahara/ Photo by
Grant Imahara

resembled a futuristic ice sculpture—check out the photos at www.teamdeadblow.net. ("I had to throw it out, because it was taking up too much space," Grant says. "But everyone yelled at me for doing that.") If you're as exacting about building a full-scale model as Grant is, you might be able to use your prototype components as guides to machine the parts for your robot. Prototypes also help builders test complex movement. "I usually just draw my designs on paper or in the computer," says Team Sinister's Mark Setrakian, "but I had to build a prototype for Mechadon's legs to figure out the proper geometry to make the movement work." A good prototype can also serve a promotional purpose too, says Team Coolrobots' Christian Carlberg: "You can use it as tool to get other people's interest." You might want to build a working model, suggests bot builder and engineer Dave Thau, "because that'll be cheaper and then you can see if you enjoy the process."

Art smart

Your prime prototype directives are simple: don't burn yourself out at this early stage, and give yourself some creative license. Team Carnivore's Ilya Polyakov builds prototypes in wood. Mark Setrakian worked out his ideas for Mechadon's movement with tounge depressors, hot glue and servos. Just don't go all *Close Encounters* on us and start modeling stuff out of mashed potatoes—your materials should hold their shape well enough for you to examine your prototype at length and learn from it. Once you have every last detail committed to paper/wood/tounge depressors/pixels/acrylic/metal/other durable stuff, you can scrutinize your plan for everything that could possibly go wrong—and doctor your design accordingly.

We learn more by looking for the answer to a question and not finding it than we do from learning the answer itself.
— Lloyd Alexander

Testing, **one,** two . . .

When putting your design to the test, emulate Santa Claus: Make a list, and check it twice. Looking at your design, jot down all the design flaws and potential strategic weaknesses. You want your bot to be naughty, not nice. Then go back and modify your design accordingly. Once you're done, look over your list again, and see how many flaws and weaknesses you can check off. Satisfying, isn't it? Now do it again.

My, aren't
we testy

How do you know when you've got a combat-ready design? Rack your brains—that's what they're there for—and consult Jim Smentowski's design checklist (courtesy www.robotcombat.com):

- If your robot is inverted, can you flip back over or still drive upside down? If not, you might be vulnerable.
- If your bot can't drive upside-down or flip back over, what about your defense to scooping or flipping robots? Can you put on armor skirts that almost meet the floor to avoid such attacks?
- What about your robot's sensitive electronic components? Are they designed to be located deep inside your robot, or are they near the outside where they could be damaged by an attack? Are your wires loose enough that components can shift and still stay plugged in?
- What about shock absorbing? Can your robot withstand massive impacts from the side, top, even bottom? Try it out to make sure! Push it to the limit in practice. If things break, beef them up.

- How about functionality, shape, style?
- Do you want your robot to perform a certain task? Build it around your idea and see what happens!

It is neither wealth nor splendor, but tranquility and occupation, which give happiness.
— Thomas Jefferson

Financing

So now that you've made it through the scheming stage, you have a terrific robot design burning a proverbial hole in your pocket. But if ideas are all you've got in your pocket, it may still be awhile before your robot gets built. The painful truth is, combat robots are an expensive pastime. The parts aren't always easy or cheap to come by, since they are typically produced in small quantities by specialty technology companies.

That could change as robots become more popular, and the market for key parts—like wheelchair motors—becomes more competitive. "Radio controllers and the motors and microcontrollers have all gotten much more accessible and affordable recently," observes bot builder and engineer Dave Thau. Who knows: robot enthusiasts may eventually drive down the price for wheelchair motors, and contribute to the development of better wheelchairs in the process. Hey, it could happen!

There is no such thing as pure pleasure; some anxiety always goes with it.
— Ovid

The cost

But until that glorious day arrives, building your own bot will cost you anywhere from $750 (a conservative estimate for a very rudimentary rookie robot) to upwards of $40,000 (for a souped-up super heavyweight). Sound like a lot? Now add the cost of batteries, plus repairs after a particularly brutal fight. Ouch. "People should know up front that you're not going to build a decent combat robot for under $750 or $1,000," cautions Team Nightmare's Jim Smentowski. "If you can't dedicate that much to it, it's probably not a good idea to start building yet—start saving, yes, but don't start building. I've heard of so many people who think they can do it for next to nothing and then run out of money, get frustrated and abandon the project. It's better to do more research, continue looking around for cheap parts, and build when you're ready."

Ignore price tags

When you're trying to develop a cost estimate for your design, don't go looking at the price tags other builders assign to their robots. "People lie about how much they spend on their robots," reveals Inertia Labs' Reason Bradley. Some builders have spent $70,000 + on their robots, but they're understandably reluctant to admit this fact to fans, who tend to root for the less expensive, underdog robots. So for a realistic estimate, just add up the cost of your desired parts and tools—and prepare to be shocked by the sheer heft of the sum.

That's why they call it disposable income

"People always underestimate how much building a robot will cost," says Grant Imahara.

"I made the decision early on that the robot gets whatever the robot

wants, so a lot of my disposable income has gone into Deadblow. I spent over $20K on the original version of Deadblow, and that's with me doing all the machining myself in a well-equipped shop. Out of the $20,000 I've spent on Deadblow, maybe $2,000 in parts are actually in the robot and another $10,000 worth didn't work out. I'll use those parts in some robot eventually—but you have to be prepared to test out a lot of parts that just don't work."

Elbow-deep in R2D2: How Grant Imahara earns money for robot parts
Photo courtesy ILM

The high prize of life, the crowning glory of a man is to be born with a bias to some pursuit which finds him in employment and happiness.
— Ralph Waldo Emerson

The payoff

PUTTING THE FUN BACK INTO WAR

DÍOTOÍR

SOFT ON THE OUTSIDE   HARD ON THE INSIDE

Watch your back: Team Díotoír gets entrepreneurial with a nifty logo
Photo courtesy of Team Díotoír

By now, this much should be clear: Robot combat is a sport, not a get-rich-quick scheme. In fact, robotics is one of the few fields in advanced technology that is more focused on adventure than money. Most bot builders aren't in it for the big bucks; they're in it for a good time and a riotous round of applause from their peers (though the adulation of millions of fans via TV is certainly a bonus). That said, your robot could pay for itself (and then some) if it's very successful. Besides the prize money for winning bots and potential sponsorships, you may be entitled to residuals if your bot appears on TV. If your bot proves to be both telegenic and tough, toy companies may take an interest in making toys based on your bot—toys of BattleBots® champs are already hitting the market.

Life as a robot superhero

As your bot gains notoriety, don't be surprised if people begin to recognize you on the street. Some builders are even parlaying personal appearances at conventions and tradeshows into regular paying gigs. "Before robots, I was a performing magician; I entertained at parties and corporate events," says Robotica® winner Mark Joerger. "Now, everyone asks how the robot is doing. I still do a few magic shows when I can wedge them in, but I think I could get more bookings just taking the robot out for exhibitions." But (you knew there had to be a but!) before you can get your bot on TV or at tradeshow booths, you have to get the thing built.

> *Determination and commitment to an unrelenting pursuit of your goal—a commitment to excellence—will enable you to attain the success you seek.*
> *— Mario Andretti*

The great scavenger hunt

We won't lie: Winning the lottery would be a terrific boost for your bot. But you don't really need the big bucks. All you need is love—that, and a whole lot of parts. Christian Carlberg today has a champion bot,

Minion, that is valued into the tens of thousands of dollars—but he started out building with the resources that were available to him. "You can afford to build things as you plan them if you have more money," he says. "But you can also work within your means, with whatever you find in a junkyard or your garage—and you'll find that within a year you'll be doing well with your bot."

If you have titanium tastes on a tin budget, don't despair. As builder and teen mentor Nola Garcia reports: "All of the kids at [nonprofit teen builders' workshop] Starbots wanted to build robots from titanium, but it's hard to find and really expensive. So we went to an airplane parts shop, and found hard steel that works almost as well—and it's much cheaper. Plus they're learning to manage their budgets and be resourceful." Many bot builders fin virtue in the necessity of scavenging for parts. "I find that it's a good challenge to see what I can make from stuff I find lying around," says teen bot builder Alex Burke. "Old stereos and VCRs have gears and lots of plastic parts that you can make into the exact size that you need."

A good (cheap) part is hard to find

It's a common myth that cheap robot parts are hard to find—they're everywhere. The trick is finding the *right* cheap robot part. That takes time, and imagination. "When you get into robot building, you start to look at everything around you and think: 'That could be a robot,' " says Jim Smentowski, who built his champion Nightmare around a huge aluminum disc he got at a salvage yard. "Sure, you can

Meaner than a junkyard dog: Nightmare
Photo courtesy of Jim Smentowski/
Photo by Jim Smentowski

build a bot completely from parts you order on the Internet, but you can't actually hold the stuff in your hand or test it out first, and you have to pay shipping on top of all that. Start locally first. Look for stuff around the house. Ask people if they're throwing stuff out. Go to the junkyard. Visit the dump. Visit the surplus yards. Going down the aisles of these places you'll see so many possibilities that'll jog your imagination. You'll find motors and batteries, car parts, windshield wiper motors, fan motors, armor panels, switches, gears, sprockets—all kinds of stuff that you can put into a robot. It's a great place to get creative, and to stay cheap." For more leads on reasonably priced parts, check out the tips and supplier links on Jim's Web site: www.robotcombat.com.

Keep $ = Lose time

There's a time/money tradeoff to building bots with scavenged or bargain-basement parts. "A lot of builders use surplus parts because it's cheaper that way," warns Grant Imahara, "but you should be aware that you could spend weeks trying to make those parts work. If you buy the correct part to begin with, you could end up saving yourself a lot of time." The Infernolab's Jason Bardis also warns builders to proceed with caution on cheap parts. "If you cut corners, nine times out of ten your bot will suffer," he warns. But there is an upside to this equation, he says: "If you do build a cheap bot, you'll learn tons." Team Strange BRU's Chuck McManis agrees. "Spending time painstakingly disassembling and reassembling a motor from a powered wheel chair can give you both a motor you need and the expertise to fix it when it breaks."

Still, skimping on a speed controller in particular could cause you unnecessary anguish when it's fighting time. "Even if you build a pretty decent bot and control it with relays, you can't drive it very well at all," cautions Jim Smentowski. "It comes down to the stresses in the arena. You need the best controls possible." Team Coolrobots' Christian

Carlberg concurs: "Spend the money on a good electronic speed controller; as long as you have that you can always upgrade the rest."

*Let me tell you the secret that has led me to my goal:
My strength lies solely in
my tenacity.*
— Louis Pasteur

Bot budgeting

Most builders live by the credo "buy what you can, when you can." Where there is a remote-controlled will, there seems to be a way to budget for parts. You've already made the commitment to your robot; it would be a shame if you let money come between you. You do the math: building a bot will probably cost you less than you spend on a week's

Mike and Lisa Winter with lightweight terror Tentoumushi
Photo courtesy Winter family/Photo by Becky Winter

vacation, less than you've spent on other toys (speedboat, motorcycle, entertainment center, stereo, you name it), maybe even less than you spent on evenings out over the last month. For some, building a bot might only require a fraction of a paycheck...OK, maybe two, or ten. Figure out what your means are, and build within them.

"But I'm broke!" protest some of you out there (you know who you are). "I'm a youngster with a five-figure loan, not an engineer with a six-figure salary!" So what, are you trying to tell us students or twentysomethings can't be bot builders? Try telling that to champs Jason Bardis, Lisa Winter, Reason Bradley, and Ilya Polyakov. Come on—your imagination is limber enough to produce a robot, so you should be able to stretch it far enough to come up with a few moneymaking schemes. Five tried-and-true techniques for young 'uns in need of some bot bucks are below; let these spark your own ideas.

Practice the art of financial self-deception

Set up direct deposit for your paycheck, and have the bank automatically transfer $100 a month into a savings account (or whatever you can afford without being obliged to live on mac-n-cheese). Now just pretend that you earn that much less, and spend accordingly. Think of it as an opportunity to relive your college days, when pepperoni on your pizza was an extravagance. Cultivate nostalgia for your childhood, when your allowance was a bright shiny quarter and Old Man Rodgers paid you a buck to mow his five-acre lawn. Play whatever head games you need to embrace your newfound cheapness—you'll have a bad-ass bot to show for it soon enough.

Trade a human vice for a robot virtue

Warning: Only the iron-willed should attempt this. This approach will test your commitment to robots for sure—but it could also do you some good. So here goes: Do you smoke a pack a day? That's $5 that could go toward a fear inspiring pulverizing arm. Drink cappuccino? That's another $3 toward a battery pack. Pint of ice cream? Consider it $4 towards tires. An hour in an arcade? If your hand-eye coordination is as lame as ours, that's easily $5 that could be spent on a motor. Video rental? $3. Overdue video? $3. You get the picture.

Don't be shy about
those gift suggestions

Got a birthday coming up? A wedding? A bar/bat mitzvah? Let your friends and family know that what you'd really like is a contribution toward your robot, or a particular part. "My parents fund all my creations, but I also mow lawns for money to buy parts and use all my Christmas and birthday money on robots," says 15-year-old bot builder Alex Burke. Consider that 30-something engineer Dave Thau got his start In bot-building with birthday funds too.

Recruit like-minded
(and financially endowed)
teammates

This really isn't as crass as it sounds, honest. Remember when you were a kid, and you used to play with Jimmy down the block just because he had cool toys—and how after awhile, you actually began to like the guy? Or how you went to a co-worker's barbecue because you couldn't say no, and wound up having a good time? Well, finding bot-building teammates can be a lot like that. Maybe you initially partner with a science department at a local school or a friend at an engineering company because you need their resources—but by the time you get done building a bot together, you will have a lot more in common than just resources. Ask any combat bot team: building and fighting bots is a uniquely bonding experience. Just be honest about your motives for proposing a partnership up front, and be sure you let your partners in on the fun stuff too (like driving).

Think of it as a **student loan**

Building a robot is an invaluable crash course in mechanics, engineering, communication, and technology that will broaden your skills set and your horizons. "Spending the money to build a robot is really an investment in education," explains bot builder and youth mentor Nola Garcia. So put up the money you need to enroll in Robot University (or ask your parents to), and give yourself several years to recoup the costs. You might not even need to wait that long, according to Nola: "When we showed Intel what our Starbots [community builders' program] kids had been inventing, they were so excited. They told us, 'That's an amazing pool of talent we'll want to hire. They've got the range of technical and communication skills we urgently need.'"

Sponsorship

And now, a word from your sponsors…hey, that's your cue! Until your first bot is actually built, your main sponsor will probably be you. "Many competitors believe that there is a line of corporations just waiting to shower money on them if they declare they are building a robot and looking for sponsorship," says Dan Danknick of Team Delta (www.teamdelta.com). "It just ain't so. The single most important requirement for obtaining sponsorship is having a robot to show off your ability to deliver. Few people are willing to sponsor intent. So don't rule out that in your first year, you alone will have to pay all of the bills in order to have something to take around and show off for the next year."

Another good reason to stay in school forever

There are exceptions to the "first bot, then bucks" rule, of course—but they're mostly college students. First-time builders that are also full-time students may be able to appeal to their school for resources and funding. "I was pursuing my Ph.D. in Santa Barbara and had a huge machine shop at my disposal," says Infernolab's Jason Bardis of his first robot-building experience. "I piggybacked on some department funding for undergrads to build Robot Wars® entries, so it all fell into place that

Mechanical maestros: Christian Carlberg and Jason Bardis work on Mini Inferno
Photo courtesy The Learning Channel, Inc.

year and I competed." But don't be surprised if your school balks at bankrolling a multi-thousand dollar bot. "The hardest thing is to get backing for a new design by a new builder—especially when you don't even have a bot to show them!" says Blade Runner builder and college student Ilya Polyakov. Jason agrees. "Without experience, you're not likely to get investors, unless you have similar experience with cars, non-combat robotics, R/C cars/planes, or machining to prove you're capable," he says.

Build your
robot resume

Once you've developed your robot resume a bit, your sponsorship options begin to open up. "Some people are really good at talking themselves up—they've hardly built anything, and they've got all this free stuff," says Inertia Labs' Reason Bradley. "But if you build one and you do well with it—if you can say 'We placed 106th out of this last event'—then you've got a better chance." Thanks to Toro's record of wins, Reason and his partner Alexander Rose have landed sponsorships for tires and radio controllers for Toro and T-Minus. "But for the most part we've had to front the money for parts ourselves. Before it was on TV, we really had to spend a lot of time chatting people up about it and they just said, 'Gee that sounds neat—we'll think about it,' " Reason says. "Now some people are getting back to us about sponsorship."

Those elusive
big bucks

Christian Carlberg and Ilya Polyakov hit the big time in the Big Apple
Photo courtesy Team Carnivore

Newbies may have to pay their dues before they score major sponsors. A few long-time champions have been able to give up their day jobs to pursue robots full-time, but most newbies' first corporate sponsors are still small-scale companies that provide components, not cash. Ilya Polyakov, whose bot Blade Runner is sponsored by Snapple®, is one of few competitors with backing from outside the fields of technology and entertainment. Of course, that is changing as the popularity of the sport grows, and companies recognize an opportunity to get their logo seen on TV. Several large companies have stepped forward with sponsorships in the last couple of years, including: Sony, Tivo, Seagate, Loctite, PTC, W.M. Berg, Minolta, Grainger, Bosch, Boeing, Briggs and Stratton, Maxis, Industrial Light & Magic, Parker Hannifin, and Radio Shack.

Starting out

When you're seeking your first sponsors, look close to home. Most sponsored competitors get their financial backing from their employers, friends, and family. "Start with people you know and friends of friends, as well as businesses that work with your company or school," recommends Jason Bardis of Infernolab. Your gift of gab will come in handy too, he says: "A sponsor wants some advertising in return, so show that you've got a good chance of getting them some exposure." Just be sure that the backing you're offered is really worth your while, as Jim Smentowski notes on www.robotcombat.com: "Make sure your sponsorship is worth more than the cost to enter a sponsored robot into BattleBots® as opposed to a non-sponsored bot. If you get sponsored for $200 worth of parts and nothing more, it's not worth it because your extra entry fee will negate the whole thing."

Hitting up big corporations

Once you've got bragging rights to a bad-ass bot and a marketing pitch to go with it, then you can look beyond your immediate circle for sponsors. How is this done? "Sending an e-mail about sponsorship will almost never work," says Jim Smentowski. "Call or visit them in person." Team Carnivore's Ilya Polyakov wholeheartedly agrees. "Call, call, call!" he says. "You pretty much need to become a telemarketer to get through to any company. Do research, find out who to talk to and what they want to hear. If it is a marketing person, don't even bother explaining how much horsepower your motors will have—explain how much exposure you can get them. Find out when they are releasing their next product and what its target demographic is. You need to know what they can gain from sponsoring you, and make that clear to them. Do well in competition; this gives you something to back up your offer of exposure."

Robot Marketing 101

As soon as you start talking to major corporate sponsors about backing your champion bot, you're in a whole different bucks bracket. "I wouldn't call anything less than $5,000 cash a 'sponsorship,'" says Carlo Bertocchini. "Our minimum level of sponsorship is $10,000 per year, and that will probably double next year." But landing coveted corporate sponsorships requires careful strategy, as Tony Buchignani of Hazard and War Machine fame points out on www.teamdelta.com. "Things to consider when looking for sponsorship are your team's reputation, whether you have a website and how it can enhance the image

April and Fon Davis model Mouser-wear
Photo courtesy April Davis

of the sponsor, and finally your performance at the event. As this new sport gains visibility the top sponsors are going to have their pick of teams, so you want to work on something that makes yours stand out." To show your prospective sponsors that you mean business, come prepared with visuals. "Make design drawings, and most importantly make renderings of your project with their logos on it!" says Ilya Polyakov of Blade Runner fame. "How you market yourself is really the determining factor of whether you will get the deal."

Keeping up with the
Joneses' robot

If corporate sponsorships sound like a lot of work, that's because they are. But they come in very handy once your robot's needs exceed your means. "The whole sponsor thing helps me keep up with other builders budget wise," says Ilya Polyakov. "These people are professional engineers and even Internet CEOs. How else can a college student match the money they like to spend on their toys? I have learned much since my first bot, and more funding is required to match my skills and experience. Instead of using a $40 Home Depot torch I now use $5,000 TIG welders, and instead of using random machine screws I now spend more on quality hardware."

Those whose ranks are united in purpose will be victorious.
— Sun Tzu

Conspiring

Sponsors and budgets and junk—oh my! By now it should be dawning on you that you're not in the design phase anymore, and you'll need some help to ease on down the road to competition. Robots don't obviate the need for human companionship—if anything, they increase it. Partners play an important role, since speed and a wide range of specialized skills are essential to get a bot ready in time for competition.

But let's just say for the sake of argument that you're a loner, a rebel, and you manage to get your bot done in time to compete all by yourself. Then you haul your creation to the competition, lug it into the arena, and drive your way to victory. "Ha!" you mutter to yourself, in self-congratulatory loner fashion. "I did it my way!" So you did. But then you have to fix up your robot, and do it again.

Fame, fortune—and logistical nightmares

As you advance toward the semifinals and finals, you'll have less time between matches to fix your robot and get in line for combat—possibly as little as 20 minutes. With each match you win, you'll discover new demands on your time: media, fans, potential sponsors, and other builders will all want to know how you pulled it off. "It all happens in such a condensed time frame," recalls Grant Imahara. "You fight, you do your exit interview, and you talk to fans almost all at once. When you're in the pits, you spend about half your time talking to press, fans, and kids. It's pretty tough to talk to everyone when you're trying to diagnose an axle problem." Suddenly scheduling quality time with your robot becomes difficult. If you have more than one bot in competition, sleeping and eating can become a distant memory. And if you succeed, the attention doesn't stop after the competition ends. "When I'm on TV, I get 15 e-mails a day," says Lisa Winter, builder of Mecha Tentomoushi.

I am only one; but still I am one. I cannot do every-thing, but still I can do something; I will not refuse to do the something I can do.
— Helen Keller

Recruiting

You don't have to go it alone. Most champion builders work in teams that include specialists who help with logistics, repairs, and driving. "It's a two-person or three-person operation just to move the robot," says Carlo Bertocchini of BioHazard fame. Carlo credits David Andres for help with technical repairs, and his wife Carol as Team BioHazard's road manager. "Building and running the robots isn't all there is to think about with competitions—there's also travel, accommodations, and food, plus tolerance of my long hours in the garage. Luckily I can count on Carol. She's my manager in robots—and in life too, I guess." Champions like Carlo have their pick of eager builders as teammates—but you shouldn't expect prospective teammates to be lining up at your garage door from the get-go. You've got to recruit them.

A family affair

When recruiting teammates, most bot builders start close to home—often in their home. Parents, spouses, and kids, beware: a bot-builder's enthusiasm is highly contagious, and in some cases it appears to be genetic—most notably in the case of Robot Action League builders Mike, Lisa, and Rik Winter and the many other Winters they're corralled into

Like father like daughter: Chuck and Ellen McManis tinker with Killer B
Photo courtesy The Learning Channel, Inc.

the sport. Parental oversight is required for minors, so most teen competitors like Lisa Winter spend more time with their parents building robots than they ever had before—and they don't even seem to mind. "No competitive robot is a single person affair, even if you do all the work!" explains Killer B's Chuck McManis, whose 11-year-old daughter Ellen is a key teammate. "Remember that, keep your friends and family informed, and they will be the best support group you can have. And you will need support, because it's a lot of work!" But as Team Robot Widows' Gillian Blood warns, "Don't expect your other half to help you build the robot if he's also a roboteer. Our other halves are so busy and engrossed in their own robots that they have little time to give us—not that they don't want to. Geoff, Jenny's hubby, has been particularly supportive whenever he can, when he's not helping to develop Scorpion."

Today's Tom Sawyer

Builders quickly get over any initial shyness about asking friends and colleagues for help when it comes time to build and compete. "I'm lucky that pulling together the Deadblow team was so easy," says builder Grant Imahara of his dream team (check out their unbelievable bios at www.deadblow.net). "These guys are masters at what they do. Most of us work together at ILM, so it's often just a matter of me saying, 'Hey, help me out here after work and I'll buy you a beer.' I'm familiar with the specialties of everyone in the ILM shop, so I know whom to approach for what." To sweeten the deal, ask not only what your teammates can do for you, but what you can do for your teammates. "Brian Dewe is an ace welder, so I knew I had to rope him in," says Grant. "In return, I helped him build a barn for his Rottweilers."

Know your needs

To develop a winning team, you have to have the humility to know what you don't know —and then seek out someone who does. "In robotics, you have to learn from others," says autonomous bot prodigy Alex Burke. "If anyone is willing to help you out, take their advice—you can learn from their experience and their mistakes. Take anything you can get. You never know what piece of information you're going to wind up using." If your technical advisor is close to home, so much the better, says Gillian Blood of Team Robot Widows. "Fiona and I live 200 miles round trip from [our teammate] Jenny, and have to travel over to her every other weekend or so. It can become very tiring. We've even had to post robot parts to each other to be worked on."

The journey is its own reward.
— Homer

Teambuilding

Once you have your team together, you'll need to keep it that way. "Teambuilding is important," says Nola Garcia. "Have a common goal, be all for one and one for all, be a part of the solution—and friendships will be made." As Fiona Mason says, "Maximum communication is required among team members, so that each member is allocated their tasks and knows exactly their contributions. It's a sense of healthy competition and being part of a team I think that inspires most!"

Work it on out: Adriana Bermudez, Yvonne Feliciano, Judith Martinez, Sergio Sanchez, and Danny Espinosa discuss design details
Photo courtesy Starbot/ Photo by Nola Garcia

The more,
the merrier

Once teams start submitting multiple entries to competition, they often find they need to recruit additional teammates. Just ask Gage Cauchois, who competed with Vladiator and Vlad the Impaler in Season 3 of BattleBots®: "I learned the hard way how important it is to have multiple drivers. I thought I'd compete in the loser's melee with Vlad the Impaler—but at the time the melee happened, I was standing in line waiting for Vladiator to fight." Even the master of The Master can use a hand around the shop from time to time: "I had friends and co-workers all helping out with machining the basic, modular parts for Mechadon," says Team Sinister's Mark Setrakian. "I don't always demand that my teammates are already experts."

When recruiting teammates to contend with multiple entries, however, champions caution that newbies can't always handle a pro's workload. Only a seasoned competitor like Nola Garcia could have pulled off her job in season three of BattleBots®: She was responsible for helping out with Team Loki's four entries, plus her own entry Buddy Lee Stay in Your Seat. "We had 3 robots in the queuing line at one time," she remembers. In a strange twist of fate, Buddy Lee wound up fighting Team Loki's Turbo—and winning. How did Nola manage to stay in fighting form with all her responsibilities? "Well, I can tell you there wasn't much sleep involved!" she laughs.

Hanging with the pros

If recruiting seasoned team members is difficult at first, hang in there. The longer you're in the sport, the more robot-builders you'll know— and the greater your pool of expertise to draw from. "You'll soon find yourself surrounded by other robot builders," comments Grant Imahara. "Gage Cauchois and I have the same landlord, who advertised that he was looking for artists and robot-builders to fill the space. I pulled in Jaime from Team Blendo to help with Deadblow after we started going to the junkyard together to find robot parts. Fon Davis, who also helps with Deadblow, is the builder of Mouser Mecha Catbot. Robot-building advances rapidly from a hobby into a lifestyle."

Get a good idea and stay with it. Dog it, and work at it until it's done right.
— Walt Disney

Building

Team Díotoír hard at work into the wee hours of the night
Photo courtesy of Team Díotoír/Photo by Pete Redmond

You've got a design, you've got financing, you've got a team…now all you need is a robot. Sure, it's easier said than done—but you've come too far to start being intimidated now. So here's what you'll need to get started: time, safety precautions, parts, tools, and technique. Once your robot is underway, you'll get in a groove—and you may find you never want to leave. "This robot combat thing can take over your life—be careful with it!" says Robotica® champ Mark Joerger. "I thought that I could build a robot, compete once, and then hang up my hat and move on. When I told some of the other teams about this, they just laughed and told me, 'There's no quitting robots.' They may be right."

One never notices what has been done; one can only see what remains to be done.
— Marie Curie

It's all a matter of time

You're ready to build your robot; the moment of truth has arrived. Actually, it will be more like several thousand moments. "It always seems to surprise people how much work it takes to build a robot," says autonomous bot builder Alex Burke. "They think all it takes is going out and buying a board and a motor." Team Fembot and Team Loki member Nola Garcia agrees. "People don't realize what goes into building a robot. Before competitions, we're often working until three in the morning, and then we all have to get up to go to our jobs. It's a huge commitment." "Building a robot is a lot harder than people think," confirms Team Coolrobots' Christian Carlberg. Then he adds: "All the more reason to get started right now!"

The scramble behind the scenes

The pros make robot building seem easy on TV, of course—but then most people don't see what goes on in the pits at competitions. "At one point or another, everyone except Carlo Bertocchini has come to a competition with a robot that is not quite finished," discloses Deadblow builder Grant Imahara. "There's so much going on and so many distractions that you don't want to be building your robot at the competition," explains Carlo, builder of longtime BattleBots® heavyweight champ BioHazard. "Some people are working up until the last minute, usually because they underestimated the amount of time a step would take to complete. Once they're in the pits, they may find out that they need certain parts they didn't bring with them." The same is true at Robotica®, according to Robotica® winner Mark Joerger: "I've seen a number of teams show up at events with unfinished robots that they attempt to put together at the last minute. This does not work. Run Amok was completed and ready for testing only three days before we had to ship her out for Robotica®, but I found and corrected several problems with her in that short period that would have been fatal in competition."

200 **or** 2000 hours?

Exactly how many hours should you set aside to work on your robot? As many as you've got—and then some. Sure, Reason Bradley and Alexander Rose finished their robots in record time—"Toro took 3 weeks of working nights, and T-Minus took 2," Reason reports. But consider that Reason has been welding since he was 8, has built robots for 12 years, and builds industrial robots at his day job. And consider also that Gage Cauchois, who is a lighting designer and technician with decades of technical experience, took 2000 hours developing Vlad the Impaler.

Easy **does it**

Details, details, details: Grant Imahara labors over Deadblow's design
Photo courtesy Grant Imahara

"Ah, but I'm a quick study," you say. "I bet I could get my robot done in half the time of other builders." Perhaps you could—but that doesn't mean you should. "One piece of advice I'd give beginners is don't rush through a step just to get it done," says teen bot builder Alex Burke. "If you do that, you'll make a lot of errors and miss out on learning the correct way to get through a task. You can't rush it." Don't expect to be the model of efficiency right away. "When I say get started as soon as possible, what I'm really saying is start making mistakes as soon as possible," says Team Coolrobots' Christian Carlberg. "With every mistake you make, you'll discover new ways to do things and more efficient ways to get tasks done."

Besides, one of the greatest satisfactions of robot building is taking the time to get your robot right. How many times in work or school have you had to rush through a task just to get it done—and then thought, "I could have done that better if I'd only had the time?" This is your big chance. "Building machines and letting myself enjoy that process has been for me at least as important as the actual competition, if not more important," notes Mark Setrakian of Snake, Mechadon, and The Master fame. So allow yourself enough time, and do yourself proud.

An inconvenience is an unrecognized opportunity.
— Confucious

Safety first, last, and always

Go ahead and roll your eyes; we know how you feel about safety lectures. You were bored stiff during safety drills at school. Who wasn't? We all knew the probability was slim that a tornado, hurricane or earthquake would actually hit the school—and if it did, cowering under a desk wasn't really going to help anyway. But when you're in a workshop surrounded by very powerful, heavy, and incredibly sharp machines and objects, the chance of disasters happening increases dramatically—and safety measures suddenly become a lot more interesting and relevant.

Fair warning

Most bot builders have at least one safety lesson they learned the hard way, but we want you to beat those odds. Minors must not go near a machine without explicit parental consent and adult supervision—no exceptions. If you don't have a manual on machine shop safety, get one and keep it handy for consultation; there are perfectly good reasons (and some gruesome injuries) behind those OSHA regulations. Read and absorb all the safety precautions in the manuals that come with all your tools. Develop a strict safety check procedure for entering and leaving the shop, and follow it religiously. Don't step foot in the shop unless you're lucid,

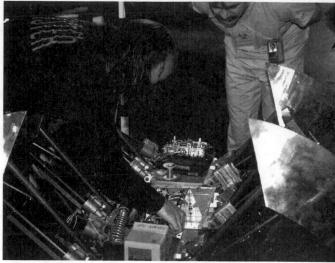

Mind the blades: Carlo Bertocchini watches as Mark Setrakian adjusts Mechadon
Photo courtesy BattleBots, Inc.®/ Photo by Garry Gay

well-fed, and well-rested. "Get enough sleep and work in an environment where there aren't a lot of distractions. You have to learn good habits in a machine shop early on—it's like a habit, like muscle memory," explains Team Sinister's Mark Setrakian. "Good safety habits become engrained." As Jenny Smith of Team Robot Widows puts it: "Don't be stupid when working. Serious accidents can and have happened. Just use your common sense."

It's all fun and
games until...

Take a page out of the book of Jason Bardis of the Infernolab, who has emerged from building five robots relatively unscathed. "I've been fortunate to have no serious injuries besides minor cuts, burns, bruises, and scrapes," he reports. "I soon realized that mufflers on gas-powered chainsaw engines get very hot very fast when running. Always put your bot up on blocks when turning it on, so it can't take off, running away from (or towards!) you. Have your weapons on a different power circuit from your drive so you can test weapons thoroughly while knowing the bot won't be moving. Always wear safety glasses—always. Try to not work alone—if you must, have somebody call or check on you every now and then. Even simple operations like drilling can turn dangerous."

May the driving **force**
be with you

Oops: Razer does a little unintended damage
Photo courtesy Team Razer/Photo by Vincent Blood

Before you jump into the driver's seat, you'll need to find a secure testing ground. "Test your robot where there is concrete all around (parking lot car blocking bars are great for this)," suggests Killer B's Chuck McManis. "If you're a spin bot, make sure there is a wall between you and the robot or you are at a different elevation. We've heard stories of spin bots losing a nut, and puncturing a hole in a car parked nearby. The absolutely best place to test your bot is in the bottom of a drained swimming pool. The surface is nice and smooth and there are walls all around."

Shocking information

When working with electronics and power tools, keep in mind the dangers posed by electrical currents and hot metal. "I've had stuff blow up and burst into flames," cautions Mark Setrakian of The Master and Mechadon fame. "My robots run on rather high voltage, but it's wise to start with commonly available 24 volts—that is a lot less likely to kill you." Momentary lapses in safety precautions can prove painful, as Gillian Blood of Team Robot Widows explains: "I was lathing some metal for our weapon, and the metal gets very hot. I picked it up without gloves on, and I burnt my finger quite badly." Your bot could be endangered by your oversights too, as Lisa Winter points out. "Check everything before you turn it on when you're building, so you don't blow anything up. Most robots have a speed controller and they're expensive. If you plug something into the battery, it could blow up the speed controller and you'd be really dinged."

RTFM +

Safety also means doing your homework. "The best safety tip I can offer is find out as much as you can about a technology before you use it, and consult as many experts as possible," says Grant Imahara of Team Deadblow. "I haven't had too many accidents—I have a machining background, and I work in a machine shop with a strict protocol for using machines in accordance with OSHA regulations. But whenever I use a technology that's new to me, I take extra precautions. Before I started working with pneumatics, I bought all the paintball magazines I could and immersed myself in researching pneumatic options for three solid weeks. Do your research—read everything you can online and in specialty magazines, and don't be afraid to ask questions."

Give me a lever long enough and a fulcrum on which to place it, and I shall move the world.
— Archimedes

Parts

Look at enough builders' workshops, and one thing becomes clear: Champion builders are usually champion pack rats. "Besides being perfectionists, we are probably the biggest junk collectors out there," admits sumo bot builder Dion Brewington. "Even some of the most insignificant items get recycled into future bots." "We're constantly going through old surplus catalogs and ordering stuff that might work," says Reason Bradley of Toro fame. "Our shelves are full of the stuff that maybe we'll use someday—it's about having stuff on hand. We dream about having drawers of parts, because the build times get a lot faster when you have the parts on hand." Pack rats don't have to be disorganized: Carlo Bertocchini's garage is lined with shelves of neatly labeled clean white boxes of resources, and sculptor/inventor Marc Thorpe's studio has hooks hanging from the ceiling to keep works in progress within an arm's reach. The point is to have parts on hand, and plenty of them.

Your parts wish list

Clean out your garage—if you're building a robot, you're going to need the room. As soon as you've cleared out a corner, you should begin to fill it up with the following basic items. Robot technology is advancing so quickly that new must-have parts are emerging even as you read this; consider this your modest starter list, and check the websites listed for updates.

Motors: Before you sink time and money into motors, learn about your specific motor needs and limitations at www.robotbooks.com/motor-tips.htm. When you know what you're after, finding motors should be relatively easy and cheap: check your local junkyards, surplus centers, and the suppliers section on www.robotcombat.com. If you want to know what a specific builder uses, go to that builder's Web page and see whether that information is disclosed—it may not be. "One of the biggest kept secrets in the sport is motor sources," says Jim Smentowski of Nightmare and Backlash fame. "When people ask I might tell them the type of motor, such as 'a 12-volt DC permanent magnet motor.' Some of the technology gets advanced so quickly that if you're one of the first to catch on to a cool new part for your bot, you want to keep it to yourself for awhile. Once people start to discover the part source, the sport can be flooded with people using it, so it's OK to want to keep some info to yourself; after all, this is a competition." Some of the best tips concerning motors are relatively common knowledge in the pits, according to Armored Robotics' Rik Winter: "You can use battery powered drills to drive wheels and weapons. Also, electric motors can run at least twice or four times the voltage. They don't run long, but they run incredibly fast. That's one of the lessons people learn all the time at BattleBots®."

Tires: If you want to win at BattleBots®, Jim Smentowski has three words for you: "Traction, traction, traction!" You'll need wide, durable rubber tires to grip the floor as you shove your opponent up against the spike strips. Research the robots that are similar in design to yours, and find out on the appropriate team Web sites what tires they use and what success they've had with them. Again, once you determine what's right for your design, you can score your tires at junkyards, surplus centers, and through the suppliers section on www.robotcombat.com.

FM or PCM radio: PCM (digital) radio is preferable, but it'll cost you. Be aware that no matter what radio you use, reception in most bot competition arenas is dismal due to all the radio interference and metal—so pick up a few tips at www.robotbooks.com/robot-electron-ics-tips.htm and do what you can to improve your radio reception. If you're looking for leads on where to find radios, go to www.coolrobots.com.

Batteries: There are a plethora of choices out there; choose wisely. You could end up weighing down your robot with battery packs or not giving your bot enough juice. "Most BattleBots® contestants use lead acid gel cells," says Carlo Bertocchini at www.robotbooks.com/robot-electronics-tips.htm. But there are other options too, he points out: "To compare one battery against another, you have to consider each one of the following parameters: capacity (measured in Amp-hours), voltage, maximum rate of discharge (power), weight, size, speed of recharge, and cost. Don't confuse Amp-hours with power. Amp-hours tell us the total energy in the battery; power tells us how quickly that energy can be withdrawn from the battery."

Speed controllers: Now is not the time to be cheap. You need a reli-able speed controller, and most competitors recommend Vantec. "Vantec ends up being your most expensive part," notes Armored Robotics' Rik Winter. Since you're spending the money, you'll want your speed controller to last awhile—find out how to take proper care of your speed controller at www.robotbooks.com/robot-electronics-tips.htm.

Piles of stainless steel, aluminum, plywood, KEVLAR®, magnesium, Lexan®, titanium (you should be so lucky!): Use these materials as the basis for your chassis and armor. Notice that's *materials*, plural: "The trick is to use the lightest material of sufficient strength for each component," explains Carlo Bertocchini. Check out the comparative strengths, current availability and cost of high-performance materials at www.robotbooks.com/robot-materials.htm for starters. You don't have to go for the highest-ticket materials, though: "You don't have use expensive KEVLAR®, aluminum, or stainless steel; you can really use mainly cheap stuff," says Armored Robotics' Rik Winter. "You *can* use plywood as a base and hose clamps to hold the drills to the plywood. Plywood is not the lightest thing in the world, but it is incredibly strong. Saws don't go well through plywood. If you want to use good plywood, use marine." If you go with cheap materials, they should be relatively easy to find; otherwise, you'll have to do your Web and catalog research.

Miscellaneous electronic components and hardware: this is what you'll use to hold components together. You know your way to your local hardware store, we presume. You may be able to scavenge some of these parts from garages, auto-supply places, junkyards, and the like.

Get it together

When the robot parts reach critical mass in your garage, start laying it out to see if your internal components will fit—without pushing you over the weight limit. If you've designed in Pro Engineer or AutoCAD you should already have a good sense of how things will fit; if not, you'll need to put your design to the eyeball test. "Get all of your internal components first before you start making the outside," recommends

The InfernoLab's Jason Bardis. "Get your motors, batteries, wheels, electronics and radio, and then place everything where it ought to fit on a paper or cardboard mock-up. Only then should you start thinking about finalizing the frame and armor." If your components meet the space test, then you need to make sure they don't weigh too much. Calculate the weight of your armor, then add

Live! Nude! Bot! Nemesis bares all
Photo courtesy Team Díotoír

the weight of each part separately. "Weigh every part before you put your robot together," advises Inertia Labs' Reason Bradley. "It's the hardest thing in the world, when you've got your robot all done and then you take to the scales and it's overweight. It's generally at the last minute, and you have to cut holes in it." Provided you're absolutely sure your parts and armor meet your space and weight limitations, you're finally ready to hit the tools.

I saw the angel in the marble and carved until I set
him free.
— Michelangelo

Tools

In the popular imagination, a robot builder's workshop is a secret laboratory filled with beakers of bubbling chemicals, Bunsen burners and at least one Theramin machine. In reality, a builder's workshop looks suspiciously like a garage (usually because it *is* a garage) crammed with scavenged parts and catalogs and a motley assortment of power tools. True, some builders have pristine workshops and state-of-the-art equipment—but you don't need that to get started. Your most valuable tool for building is your brain; once you've got that fired up, you don't

Mr. Clean: Bot builder Alex Burke in his tidy workshop
Photo courtesy Patty Burke/Photo by Patty Burke

necessarily need a lot of expensive tools to get your bot built. "I don't have a machine shop, lathe, Tig welder, and such," says Team Nightmare's Jim Smentowski on www.robotcombat.com. "I do all my construction in the comfort of my garage with ordinary power tools that you can buy from the local hardware store (with the notable exception of a small milling machine that I recently added to my shop)."

Your tool wish list

Jim Smentowski provides the following invaluable starter list of tools for robot builders on www.robotcombat.com (plus many other tips for getting started, so go there, already):

Saws - Jigsaw, circular saw, miter saw, table saw, hacksaw, band saw, reciprocating saw—all these I have and have used in the construction of my robots. You may not need all these, but remember that you'll need metal cutting blades for all the above.

Grinder & files - Invaluable to robot construction. I use my grinder every day while building robots, and what you can do with a simple file is amazing. Get a selection of files small and large, and if you have the luxury of a Dremel or air die grinder, rotary files can save a TON of time (just make sure to wear eye protection!) Oh, and don't underestimate the power of sandpaper if you're using aluminum! A belt or disc sander can come in very helpful!

Cordless drill and possibly a drill press - You NEED a drill. And get yourself some good metal-cutting grade bits, or you'll be replacing bits far too often. You'll use your cordless drill for screws and bolts too; get a screwdriver bit and socket set for it. If you plan on drilling through hard metals, you'll need some cutting fluid to keep from burning up your bits and make those cuts a lot easier.

Standard issue socket set, screwdrivers, wire cutters and crimpers, soldering iron, open end wrenches, prybar, hammer, rubber mallet, vise grips, pliers, etc. - All these you may already have; if not, get 'em!

Workbench with vise - you need a place to put your robot while working on it—working on the floor or the kitchen table is not recommended; go get a cheap Craftsman foldable bench (around $45) and stick a vise to it ($14.99). Half of my robot construction has been on a workbench like this. Oh, get some C-clamps too—they come in very handy to hold pieces down or together while you're working on them.

Welder - If you don't plan on putting the whole robot together with screws and bolts, get a welder. Arc welders are cheapest; some can be found under $100. It takes some practice, but the welds are pretty secure. Another method I've used that is not quite as strong is brazing with Mapp gass/Oxygen tanks. I've built two of my robots with this method, and the brazing holds up pretty well under most circumstances (even running into a curb at full speed!). MIG and TIG welding is the best (and most expensive) way to combine your metals—it's on my wish list too.

Camera - You need to be able to document the progress of your construction, if not to show to others at the events and on websites, then for your own journal and ability to look back at any mistakes and accomplishments. Keep a camera near your work area, and if you have a camcorder, videotape yourself working on your robot. Have someone tape you practicing your robot and repairing it. Never let a weapons test go unrecorded. There will be lots of opportunities to share this kind of recorded imagery with other builders and the media, so don't let good stuff go unrecorded!

Tools on the cheap

You can keep your tool expenditures down if you're willing to compensate for your lack of resources with learning. "It's still possible to make a fairly competitive bot with pretty simple tools," says Jonathan Ridder of Team Ziggo. "It's getting harder to be competitive if you don't have machine equipment, but you can still make a pretty competitive one using things like Lexan® (a type of bullet-proof plastic). It's easy to work with using just a circular saw and a drill and makes pretty good armor. You can make a base plate out of that and get some controllers and wheel-chair motors, which already have wheels made for them. And just strap it all down with some hose clamps or something. You can even build one using hand tools." Sounds simple—but by now you know there's a procedure behind even the simplest bot. You know the drill: Do your research, prepare your design, source your parts, team up, take your safety precautions, gather your gear, and get cracking—you'll soon have a bot to show for it.

Genius is one percent inspiration, and ninety-nine percent perspiration.
— Thomas Edison

Technique

Robot building technique is something that's developed by doing, not by reading. If you don't already have basic welding and machining skills, put down this book right now and learn some. Volunteer to help a

Rosie the Riveter's got nothing on Team Fembot's Nola Garcia
Photo Courtesy Starbot/ Photo by Bill Garcia

skilled machinist in exchange for lessons; take classes; find a community workshop where you can pick up skills in a supervised setting; intern or apprentice at a machine shop that is willing to train you; offer to help a robot building team however you can; start paying attention in shop class. Once you've picked up some basic shop skills, you'll be in a better position to build—and make smart decisions for your bot. Even if one of your team members is going to be doing most of the machining and welding and you're planning to pay someone to do the rest, you should have an intimate understanding of how assembly techniques affect your design and strategy—especially bolting and welding.

Welders v.
Bolters

Team PNTA'a Jim Stevens gets it right on a prototype
Photo courtesy of Michael Bastoni/Photo by David Cann

The world of people can be loosely divided into the cat people camp and the dog people camp; likewise, the world of robots can be divided into the welding camp and the bolting camp. Most people do some welding or bolting at some point, of course, but as a primary means of construction builders usually opt for one or the other. Neither practice asserts absolute superiority in the arena; there are some extremely rugged bots that are precision-machined and bolted down tight (think

BioHazard), and there are also some amazingly resilient bots that are mostly welded together (i.e. T-Minus and Toro).

What's your **medium?**

Your decision to weld or bolt will be as much a creative decision as a strategic one. You may choose to let your skill set dictate your approach—but then you might be missing out on learning a process you'd really enjoy and would better serve your bot. Certain designs just seem to lend themselves to using one practice over the other. BioHazard has multiple precision-machined panels that can each be replaced without requiring a complete bot overhaul. But Jonathan Ridder's Ziggo is built with a soft-steel wok shell that lends itself to quick welding repairs. Both bots are longtime champions. Ultimately— and for much the same reasons that an artist chooses one medium over another—you have to go with the process that feels right for you and your bot, given your design and levels of skill and patience.

Know the **tradeoffs**

Team Inertia Labs has tried both approaches, and sees pros and cons to each. "We originally machined every part of our robots," says Reason Bradley of Team Inertia Labs. "A simple block plate would have 10 holes, and I would machine each part on the mill. If we got a side panel smashed in, you could just bolt in a new side." This approach allowed Reason and his teammate Alexander Rose to create a very rugged robot, without seams that would expose weak areas on the bot. But there were draw-backs. "The disadvantage there is you have to build basically two robots, because you want to have spare parts. That took a lot of time, so we switched to welding. But with welding, you usually have to cut the panel out and put the new one in." With their combined expertise in welding, Reason and Alexander were able to figure out a way to make welding work in their favor with Toro and T-Minus. "We found a way to cut out a dent here, insert a piece and just weld it up, so it's a lot faster."

Comparison shopping

Cost and availability of tools may also influence your choice of assembly methods. If you choose to go with the bolt method, scan Carlo Bertocchini's www.robotbooks.com site to find out what tools the BioHazard team uses—and if you can afford them. You may want to hook up with a local school or community workshop to use their facilities for machining. If you choose to go with welding, you might want to invest in welding equipment, which tends to be cheaper than the equipment required for precision machining. Check out your equipment options online—you may find some great deals and some useful tips for building without spending a fortune.

Fighting

If you've made it this far, you must be itching for a fight. All that time in the shop, and only three to five minutes in the area. How can that possibly be worthwhile? You could ask a similar question to basketball players, artists, race car drivers, or musicians, and they'd give you the same answer as any robot builder: "I don't know—but it just *is*."

You can tell from a team's expressions in the heat of battle that their senses are heightened to skyscraper proportions. "It's crazy when you're up there on the podium driving," reports Team Nightmare's Jim Smentowski. "Nothing you can do can really prepares you for that adrenaline rush. I kind of go into a little trance mode when I'm actually on the podium with my controller. I mean, I've done it enough times that you'd think I'd be used to it. There's a lot of stress involved. You can be up against a robot that's completely dead and do something stupid. I've got a little team of people who help coach me while I'm driving during matches. They'll be right next to me screaming, 'Watch out for the saws!' and I'll be so focused I don't even hear them."

We will either find a way, or make one.
— Hannibal

Driver's Ed

Whether those few minutes on the podium are ecstasy or agony depends in large part on your team's driving skills. "A lot of new builders don't realize you could have a mediocre robot and drive it really well and go home with a [BattleBots® trophy] Nut," says Team Fembot and Team Loki member Nola Garcia.

The ultimate driver's test: The Gauntlet at Robotica®
Photo courtesy The Learning Channel, Inc.

"The bottom of Buddy Lee Stay in Your Seat is Lexan, and at a demo recently I noticed a couple of guys being sneaky, looking at the underside and doing a diagram. So I went over to them and said, 'Do you want me to help you out?' They were surprised—but the truth is, we could build the same robot and still get different results, because we'd have different strategies and drive differently."

Road testing

If your robot is not built until the night before the competition, you may not ever get a chance to crunch metal with the best of them. "New builders often don't leave themselves enough time to practice driving before competitions," observes Nola Garcia. "When you drive your robot, you might find out that one of your solders didn't hold." Team Deadblow's Grant Imahara warns that your strategy could suffer, too: "If you haven't practiced driving beforehand, you're not going to

187

know how to deliver your weapon to your opponent in the most efficient manner, while avoiding their weapon and the arena hazards."

The team, fans, and competition alike are disappointed when the match ends prematurely due to preventable mechanical failure—and it happens all too often. "It's the worst when one robot has mechanical failure," says Team Sinister's Mark Setrakian. "The best matches are ones where driving ability, strategy and durability are the deciding factors." Lisa Winter of the Robot Action League concurs: "Most people get in there and their bot doesn't work, or it's just a slow fight because they don't know how to drive."

Brace for
impact

To expose potential engineering flaws, drivers should test for impact in addition to maneuverability. "Everybody's scared to break their bot before the show," says Jason Bardis of the Infernolab. "You need to practice hitting stuff to see what breaks and where the weak link in the chain is." "Your robot must be able to withstand a *serious* impact," explains Strange BRU captain Chuck McManis. "When your robot collides with an obstacle or another robot, the force can easily reach 9 or 10 G's (10 times the force of gravity!)." Bot builder and engineer Dave Thau agrees, "There are lots of times a robot will be winning, and get slammed—something will come loose and that's the end of it. . You need to have everything tied down – not with twist ties, either. Not having all of your components properly attached is a major mistake."

Life shrinks or expands in proportion to one's courage.
— Anais Nin

Seize the advantage

Driving is one area in which newbies can give champions a run for their titles—especially since changing arena hazards add an element of the unexpected to competition. "This last season, the robots were at a higher level than the previous competitions," observes Carlo Bertocchini, builder and driver of longtime heavyweight champion BioHazard. "There are more hazards in the BattleBox™ too, and there's not much room to maneuver. In the last competition, I was worried about my robot—it was hard to even get it functioning well enough to compete—so I wasn't paying as much attention to my driving." Inertia Labs has had to make structural changes to Toro to contend with changing arena hazards. "We had a lot of trouble getting caught up on curbs and in the arena, especially as they added more things to the BattleBox™," says Reason Bradley.

Have no fear

Fearless fighter: Run Amok charges into battle
Photo courtesy The Learning Channel, Inc.

Even with all the cautions about arena hazards and mechanical failures, Robotica® champion Mark Joerger says, "You cannot have any fear of your competition." Fear won't win you any fans, either, according to bot builder and fan Dave Thau. "Running away always gets the audience booing." Like many fans, Dave counts among his favorites the apparently fearless Vlad the Impaler. "I like to make noise—I guess I'm like the gorilla in the forest that shakes the branches to impress the other gorillas," admits Team Vladiator's Gage Cauchois. "I like to crash into the wall in reverse—it's a great break away from the hazards and produces a huge amount of energy I can capitalize on."

Your mind is a
lethal weapon

Like Gage, all serious competitors mastermind a fighting strategy before ever entering the arena. "All bots have weaknesses," explains RunAmok's Mark Joerger, "and it is up to the team to find and take advantage of the weakness in the other bot." "At the events, you're chatting people up and checking out their bots, looking for weaknesses," explains Reason Bradley of Toro and T-Minus fame. "Every time we know we're going up against a robot, we get a good look at it, evaluate it, and get a game plan. We do a little research on it to see where's the best place to hit it." This strategy has won Toro many fights and fans—including Gage Cauchois. "I liked watching the Toro team fight this year," he says. "They use the same approach as I do: be methodical, then go in for kill."

Work on your
moves

That said, there are no surefire maneuvers to land you a trophy. In 50 years, there may be names for the different styles of robot fighting, much as there are for martial arts practiced by humans. There might be a move called Robot Widowed or a Scorpion Meets Snake configuration that commentators will judge while the bots are in action at the first robot Olympics. There could be playbooks on bot combat strategy,

So *this* is what a winning streak looks like: Razer's trophy table
Photo courtesy Team Razer/Photo by Vincent Blood

just as there are for chess. Maybe some of these standard fighting techniques will be based on your robot, or a battle you participated in. But until then, the best ways to pick up winning moves remain practice and careful observation.

It is better to deserve honors and not have them than to have them and not deserve them.
— Mark Twain

Fight **fair**

Fairness is as important as fearlessness in winning over the audience, and audience approval accounts in large part for the rush competitors get out of a fight. When a plucky competitor competes well despite the odds—as Jason Bardis' lightweight Mini Inferno did against Mike McManus' heavyweight Killer B in Robotica®—the crowd roars, and remembers your robot. "Losing is far from the worst thing that can happen to a team, and having your bot destroyed is not a disaster either," says Robotica® winner Mark Joerger. "Failing to compete honorably is much worse."

Mini Inferno chases Killer B at Robotica®
Photo courtesy The Learning Channel, Inc.

Loopholes can be
hazardous

Winning on a technicality inevitably gets the audience booing—and prompts new rules to be made so you can't win the same way again. "I'm a Porsche fanatic, and they almost always win LeMans by reading the rulebook and finding the holes—so that's what I did," admits Shaft and KMM builder Rik Winter. "The hole in the early Robot Wars® rules was that you could pin someone and win, so all I had to do was hold someone and control the situation to win. I actually won the face-off and melee the first year I competed. I'll admit that it was slightly lame and boring cause I didn't actually destroy something. My matches actually provoked a new rule: you can't win just by pinning."

Make it a
worthy fight

The fighting code of honor extends to not taking cheap shots at your opponent, and occasionally helping a disabled competitor to finish a fight. "It's maybe good if you do it 10-20% of the time—it puts on a better show," says longtime champ and perennial crowd favorite Carlo Bertocchini, of BioHazard fame. "You can beat your opponent in 30 seconds, but if you do that you'll be missing out on that 2 1/2 minutes of fun—so you might go unstick your opponent from a hazard, and have a little bit more fun in the arena while you get a chance. I don't hold it against anybody if they decide not to do that, because it is a sport and there's actually quite a bit at stake here now, with television royalties and toy contracts and things like that. But it shows how much fun people are having that they are still doing this."

Battle Tactics

by Carlo Bertocchini and Sun Tzu

Know the Enemy

Now the reason the…wise general's…achievements surpass those of ordinary men is foreknowledge. [It] cannot be elicited from spirits, nor from gods, nor by analogy with past events, nor from calculations. It must be obtained from men who know the enemy situation. – Sun Tzu

In the 1995 FIRST competition, our team had exactly seven weeks to finish its robot and ship it to Disney World where the competition would be held. Some teams were participating in a regional competition, and they had their robots for an extra week or so before they were required to ship them to Florida. Although it was too late to make changes to our robot, we were very keen to get a glimpse of the enemy before going into battle. Unfortunately, the venue for the regional competition was about 2000 miles away. Over budget on the robot, and with travel expenses for 13 team members coming up, we couldn't afford to send a spy to the regional. However, we could afford to make a few telephone calls to find someone who would videotape it for us. The tape was grainy, the action poorly lit, and the subjects sometimes out of focus. But we watched it repeatedly, freezing the action on key frames and studying it as if we were the FBI studying the Kennedy assassination tape. We wanted to:

Probe him and learn where his strength is abundant and where deficient … determine the enemy's plans and you will know which strategy will be successful and which will not. Take advantage of the enemy's unpreparedness…and strike him where he has taken no precautions. – Sun Tzu

The national competition at Disney World was a two-day event. We had learned the strategies, strengths, and weaknesses of about one-fourth of the robots. Now was our chance to fill in the gaps in our knowledge. The pace was hectic and most of our team members were either preparing or repairing the robot all day. We staked out some front row seats and, working in shifts, we had at least two team members taking copious notes on each of our opponents. We learned which were fast and which were slow. If the opposing robot was a strong ramp-climber, but a weak ball handler, we would adjust our strategy. If the robot had a tendency to fall off the ramp, we would be there to give it a little nudge. We won every match that day and were awarded the trophy for Top Seed. The next day, with the help of our database of enemy intelligence, we won the competition! After a performance like that, they couldn't help but give us the trophy for Rookie of the Year. We may have taken it to an extreme, but we firmly believed in this advice from Sun Tzu:

Know the enemy and know yourself; in a hundred battles you will never be in peril. When you are ignorant of the enemy but know yourself, your chances of winning and losing are equal. If ignorant both of the enemy and of yourself, you are certain in every battle to be in peril.

Of course this foreknowledge business can be a two edged sword. You should take precautions that your own secrets do not fall prey to the enemy spies. Remember:

All warfare is based on deception. Therefore, when capable, feign incapacity...Pretend inferiority and encourage his arrogance. – Sun Tzu

These lessons have not been lost on modern day robot combatants. If you search the Internet you will find many pictures and descriptions of competition robots. You will also find that some people are not so forthcoming with details of their design. Some offer only tantalizing hints of the capabilities of their robots. Photographs provided are extreme close-ups or distant and unfocused—just enough to portray a serious competitor, but not good enough for a spy to gain an advantage.

Heed the words of Sun Tzu and you will have an edge over those who fail to do so.

Exerpted from "The Art of Robot War:
Ancient Words of Wisdom for Modern Robot Battles"
By Sun Tzu and Carlo Bertocchini
©1998, Carlo Bertocchini
Originally published in January 1999 issue of *Robot Science & Technology* magazine.

Go confidently in the direction of your dreams! Live the life you've imagined.
— Henry David Thoreau

Fightin' Words:
A starter list of terms you might hear slung around the pits.

Activate: Term that denotes the start of a battle. [Jenny Smith]

Amazonian Hardwood: Tongue-in-cheek name for aluminum. [Chris McVey]

Autonomous: Put simply, no external human intervention. BattleBots® are driven by radio control and are not considered autonomous. Autonomous robots have all the decisions made by the micro controller. All reactions are prepro-grammed by the designer, giving the robot a life of its own. [Jason Bardis]

Box of sparks: Battery. [Team S.L.A.M.]

Bot BAD: Bot Builder And Designer. [Tony Somerfield]

Bot: Short for robot or BattleBot™. A machine used in combat against another machine. [Chris McVey]

Box: As in the BattleBox®; refers to the BattleBots® arena. [Chris McVey]

CAD: Computer Aided Design or, in many cases, Cardboard Aided Design. [Ilya Polyakov]

Car steering: Steering using wheels that change their angle of rotation like a car. [Chris McVey]

Carlo: Affectionate term for a motor. [John Kruse]

Cease: Supposed to mean stop. Not always observed. [Jenny Smith]

Clampbot: A type of robot that employs pincers. Diesector, Complete Control, et al. [B. Nakagawa]

Cluebie: Newbie who has some understanding of the skills and engineering needed to build a successful bot. [Richard Chandler]

Controller: Controls everything from electronic speed controls to the wireless serial control linkup used to guide some of the bots. [Ilya Polyakov]

CrewBot: The guys you see between matches wrangling robots and picking up parts. Braver men than your typical Union stagehand by far. [Richard Chandler]

Dance on the killsaws: Euphemism for when a bot takes a hit from the kill saws. [John Kruse]

Dinosaur Juice: Fuel for I/C engines. [Team S.L.A.M.]

Enough: Mythical amount of armor that will keep your bot's innards safe from Pete's [Lambertson, BattleBots® hazards operator] toys and your opponent's weapons. [B. Nakagawa]

ESC: 1. Electronic Speed Control. An electronic device used to control the speed at which the wheels turn. Often a very expensive and somewhat vulnerable piece of equipment. Popular models include the Vantec and the Victor 883. [Chris McVey] 2. Electronic Smoke Container. Slang. [Team S.L.A.M.]

EV Warrior: A reliable motor that is very popular among builders. Often found in surplus shops. [Chris McVey]

Flippers: Lifters that operate extremely fast and actually have the ability to flip opponents. Examples: Toro, T-Minus, and Chaos 2 (U.K.). [Jonathan Ridder]

Forum: A place where builders discuss things amongst themselves. [Chris McVey]

Front and rear: Driver and weapons operator. [Tony Somerfield]

Gassed up: Flipper robot ready to fight. [Tony Somerfield]

Glue: The person who breaks up all of the arguments between team members; beer works, too. [Ilya Polyakov]

Gourmet Damage: A truly spectacular hit that shreds armor and sends parts flying—especially if it happens more than once. [Richard Chandler]

Ground clearance: The gap between your robot and the floor. If it is too big, other robots can get under and flip your robot. [Pete Redmond]

Hammer bot: A robot employing a large hammer or pick as a weapon. Examples include Grendal, The Judge, and Deadblow. [Chris McVey]

Hole Punch: BattleBots® spike strip. [Team S.L.A.M.]

Hydraulic or pneumatic pressure: The amount of power you have in your weapon. Measured in bars or psi, the higher the better. [Pete Redmond]

I/C engine: Infernal combustion engine. [Team S.L.A.M.]

Involuntary inversion syndrome: "My robot got flipped over." [Jenny Smith]

IRPD: Infrared Proximity Detector. Device used to pulse infrared and then check for reflection. If a reflection is detected the sensor reports the information to the micro controller, which can choose to avoid or pursue the object. [Dion Brewington]

K.I.S.S: Keep It Simple Stupid. The ground rule for a robot. [Jenny Smith]

KILL SAW BARF: Sparks. [Team S.L.A.M.]

Kindling: Wooden bot that fights a spinner. [B. Nakagawa]

Knock-off: Bot obviously inspired by a successful predecessor. Clone. [B. Nakagawa]

Lifters: Bot with the ability to lift other bots, get their drive wheels off the ground, and push them around the arena. Examples: BioHazard, Vlad the Impaler, and Voltronic. [Jonathan Ridder]

Linear Actuator: A device used to produce back and forth motion. Often used in lifting arms. [Chris McVey]

Magic Smoke: 1. Burnt out electrical component. Refers to the tongue-in-cheek notion that electronics are operated via magic smoke, and that when you let it out (i.e. it burns up) they no longer work. [Chris McVey] 2. Popular usage: "The speed controller doesn't work anymore because we accidentally let the magic smoke out." [Team S.L.A.M.]

Mauler Dance: Term for when a spinner gets flipped. Named after Mauler's surprising upset in season 2.0. [Richard Chandler]

Mauler Hammer: A mystical tool that robot builders use to pound the dents out of their armor plates in the pits. It is rumored that the Tilford family forged this REALLY BIG hammer themselves. I believe it says Mauler on the side. (I've used it on occasion and there's nothing better!) [Grant Imahara]

Melty Brain: The computer system that allows [robots] to spin and move translationally at the same time. It has had limited use in combat but is the next in technology at BattleBots®. Also, when the bot is spun up and guided by the Brain, it is said to be in Melty Mode. [Ilya Polyakov]

Metal: Bot. [Tony Somerfield]

Microcontroller: Programmable IC chip with input and output capabilities. Basically, the brains of the robot. Receives feedback from sensors and then outputs to the motor controls and other accessories. [Dion Brewington]

Negative telemetry situation: "Oh God, my transmitter batteries have gone flat!" [Jenny Smith]

NiCad: A type of battery approved for use in a BattleBots® entrant. [Chris McVey]

NiMH: Nickel Metal Hydride. A type of battery approved for use in a BattleBots® entrant. [Chris McVey]

NPC: National Power Chair. A manufacturer of wheelchair motors popular among builders. [Chris McVey]

One hit wonder: Spinner or bot employing a spinning disc weapon that breaks down after one hit. [B. Nakagawa]

Pits: The area where your robot can be tinkered with between battles. [Jenny Smith]

Polycarbonate: 1. A very durable plastic often used in robot construction. 2. The clear walls of the BattleBox™. [Chris McVey]

POP: Pile of parts. Describes a robot that is still just a collection of parts. [Chris McVey]

Pound'em Pete: BattleBots® pulverizer operator, Pete Lambertson (source of "The Pete Factor"). [Team S.L.A.M.]

Pulse Width Modulation: The technique of pulsing usually involved with motor control to adjust speed. Determines the ON time and the OFF time of the motor, referred to as the duty cycle. A long OFF time slows the speed of motors. The shorter the OFF time, the faster the motor spins. [Dion Brewington]

R.U.M.B.L.E: Run. Until. My. Batteries. Lose. Everything. [Team S.L.A.M.]

Revenge: "Hell hath no fury like a robot widow scorned." [Gillian Blood]

Robot widow/widower: 1. The long-suffering partner of a roboteer. [Jenny Smith] 2. Partner of roboteer who, having been badly neglected for several years, takes revenge. [Gillian Blood]

Rolling pin: A neat weapon for beating the living daylights out of flaky roboteers. Nothing to do with the art of making flaky pastry. [Gillian Blood]

S.M.I.D.S.Y: Sorry Mate, I Didn't See You. [Jenny Smith]

Self-righting: The ability of a robot to right itself if flipped. [Chris McVey]

Servo: A motor with a built in gear reduction and location sensor. Most commonly used in radio controlled toys. These can be used for precise movement or can be modified to rotate 360 degrees for drive motors. [Dion Brewington]

SLA: Sealed Lead Acid. One of the approved types of batteries for use in a BattleBot®. [Chris McVey]

Spazbot: Bot too quick for its own good. [B. Nakagawa]

Spinner or Spinbot: A robot that uses a large spinning weapon or consists of an outer shell that spins. Examples: Mauler, Ziggo, Son of Whyachi. [Chris McVey]

SPN: South Park Newbie. Someone who got interested in BattleBots® simply because it was on after South Park, and only understands how to talk smack. Opposite of cluebie. [Richard Chandler]

Sportsmanship: A personality trait exhibited by BattleBots® contestants long thought vanished from the face of the earth. Losers congratulate winners on a fight well fought, and winners sympathize with the guy whose bot they just shredded. It is most often displayed in the pits, where builders will share spare parts and assist in making sure everyone gets to compete. [Richard Chandler]

Srimech: Self-righting mechanism. [Jenny Smith]

Stompbot: See: walker. [Chris McVey]

Structural integrity failure: Being hit by Hypno-Disc. [Jenny Smith]

Tank Steering: A method of steering using wheels operating at different speeds to change direction. [Chris McVey]

Thermal endurance test: "Oh God, I'm being held over the flame pit!" [Jenny Smith]

Ti: Pronounced "tye." Indicates the use of a Titanium alloy (e.g. "I've got Ti on the front and sides."). [Chuck McManis]

Toro'd: To be flipped in the air in a particularly violent way. Derived from Toro, one of the more powerful flipper robots. [Chris McVey]

Trial By Terror: Testing your bot for the first time in front of TV cameras or in your garage next to your Oxy-acetylene rig with the weapons on. [Team S.L.A.M.]

Turning circle: The amount of space you need to turn your robot 180 degrees. Two wheel or tank drive requires no space or zero turning circle, whereas car type steering requires a large space. [Pete Redmond]

Unintentional drive failure: The wheel/track fell off. [Jenny Smith]

Vantec: A particular brand of electronic speed control. [Chris McVey]

Vapor: Imaginary (a vaporbot is a robot that only exists in a builder's mind). [Chris McVey]

Veteran: A builder who has competed at least once. [Chris McVey]

Victor: A particular brand of electronic speed control. [Chris McVey]

Walker: A robot that uses walking or crawling to move itself. These robots have been allowed a larger weight allowance. [Chris McVey]

Wedgebot: A robot designed to lift and move other robots around the ring. [Chuck McManis]

Ziggo'd: To be violently ripped apart in the ring. Derived from the astonishing power of the lightweight robot Ziggo to destroy. [Chris McVey]

Resources

Forums:

BattleBots®	forums.delphi.com/BattleBot_Tech/start
Robot Wars® (UK)	www.robotwars.co.uk/forum/
Robot Wars® (US)	forums.delphi.com/robotwars/start/?sigdir=robotwars
Society of Robotic Combat	forums.delphi.com/SORC/start

Builders' resources:

BattleBots®	www.battlebots.com/bnc_tips.asp
Cool Robots	www.coolrobots.com/builders/newbie.html
Puppetmaster Combat Robotics	www.puppetmaster-robotics.com/faq.html
Robot Books	www.robotbooks.com/robot-design-tips.htm
Robot Combat	www.robotcombat.com/tips.html
Team Barracuda	http://chicksdigbattlebots.botic.com/
Team Delta	www.teamdelta.com/misccomm.htm
Team Hazard	www.legalword.com/tips.html
Team Killerhurtz	http://www.johnreid.demon.co.uk/howto/index.htm
Team Kruser	http://jkruse.home.mindspring.com
Team Rockitz	www.rockitz.com/Battlebots/Links.html
Team S.L.A.M	http://users.intercomm.com/stevenn/kiss/builder.htm
Team Saber	www.teamsaber.com/tutorial/index.html

And more!:

Android World	www.androidworld.com/	Mind boggling creations and lots of links.
Arrick Robotics	www.robotics.com/robots.html	Good stop for the robot generalist.
Bill Nye the Science Guy	www.nyelabs.com/	BattleBots® very own "Battle Caster."
Cabaret Mechanical Theatre	www.cabaret.co.uk/	A Museum of Automata (Mechanical Sculpture for the cultured robot enthusiast).
Cricket the Robot	home.earthlink.net/~henryarnold/	Learn how to make your own robotic cricket.
Dr. Joanne Pransky	www.robot.md	
Entertainment Robots	www.entertainmentrobots.com/	Rent a robot to be the life of the party!
Exploratorium	www.exploratorium.org	Take a virtual visit to San Francisco's museum of "science, art, and human perception." Archives include robot sumo wrestling and the science of skateboarding.
FloorBotics®	home.swbell.net/fontana/	Housecleaning goes hi-tech. Buy an autonomous floor cleaning robot to do your chores for you!
How Stuff Works	www.howstuffworks.com/	For the uncommonly curious.
Internet Movie Database	www.imdb.com	
LEGO®	www.lego.com/home.asp	The classic toy that inspires budding robot builders everywhere.

Machina Speculatrix	www.plazaearth.com/usr/gasperi/walter.htm	World's first robot?
Mad Scientists Network	www.madsci.org/	Got a question? Get an answer.
MIT's Artificial Intelligence Laboratory	www.ai.mit.edu/people/brooks/	Check out the genius behind Cog and Kismet: Rodney Brooks.
PBS Online Science	www.pbs.org/science	Beautiful graphics and great content.
Popular Science	www.popularscience.com/	It's popular. It's science. It's Popular Science.
Roboforge	www.roboforge.com/	Robot combat simulation. Good practice and good fun.
Robot Books	www.robotbooks.com	A robot fanatic's dream come true. General info, links, advice, toys, books, and more!
Robot Combat	www.robotcombat.com	Chock full of helpful robot combat info, resources, sport history, links and a database of registered bots.
Robot Café	www.robotcafe.com	"Live, Eat, Breathe...Robots™"
Robot Gallery	chaoskids.com/ROBOTS/robots.html	Pictures of collectible toy robots.
Robot Science & Technology Magazine	www.robotmag.com/	Read up on the latest robotics innovations here.
Survival Research Laboratories	srl.org/	"The most dangerous shows on earth."
Tech Geek	www.techgeek.com/	Robotics news and reviews.

US robot societies/clubs:

Atlanta Hobby Robot Club [AHRC]	www.botlanta.org/	Atlanta, Georgia
Central Illinois Robot Club	circ.mtco.com/	Peoria, Illinois
Chicago Area Robotics Group	www.robotroom.com/ChiBots/	Chicago, Illinois
Connecticut Robotics Society	www.ctrobots.org/	Hartford, Connecticut
Dallas Personal Robotics Group [DPRG]	www.dprg.org/	Dallas, Texas
East Bay Builders Group	www.zcstuff.com/ebg/	California, Berkeley
HomeBrew Robotics Club	www.augiedoggie.com/HBRC/	San Jose, California
Laboratory Robotics Interest Group	lab-robotics.org/	New Jersey
Long Island Amateur Robotics Club	members.aol.com/rich924/html/club.html	Long Island, New York
Miami Valley Robotics Club	www.activedayton.com/community/groups/robotclub/	Troy, Ohio
Missouri Area Robotics Society [MARS]	walden.mvp.net/~rickmoll/mars/	University City, Missouri
Nashua Robot Club	www.tiac.net/users/bigqueue/others/robot/homepage.htm	Nashua, New Hampshire
Phoenix Area Robot Experimenters	www.parex.org/index.html	Phoenix, Arizona
Portland Area Robotics Society [PARTS]	www.portlandrobotics.org/	Portland, Oregon
Robot Club of Traverse City, MI	www.wdweb.com/robotclub/index.asp	Traverse City, Michigan
Robotics Group	dpein.home.netcom.com/	Central Jersey, New Jersey
Robotics Society of Southern California	www.dreamdroid.com/default200.htm	Fullerton, California
Rockies Robotics Group	www.rockies-robotics.com/	Aurora, Colorado
San Diego Robotics Society	sdrobotics.tripod.com/	San Diego, California
San Francisco Robotics Society [SFRSA]	www.robots.org/	San Francisco, California
Seattle Robotics Society	www.seattlerobotics.org/	Seattle, Washington
Society of Robotic Combat	www.sorc.ws/	
The ISU Robotics Club	www.ee.iastate.edu/~cybot/	Iowa State University

The Robot Group	www.robotgroup.org/index.html	Austin, Texas
Triangle Amateur Robotics	triangleamateurrobotics.org/	Raleigh, North Carolina
Twin Cities Robotics Group	www.tcrobots.org/	St. Paul, Minnesota

International robot societies/clubs:

Art & Robotics Group	www.interaccess.org/arg/	Canada
Edmonton Area Robotics Society	www.ualberta.ca/~nadine/ears.html	Canada
EFREI Robotique	assos.efrei.fr/robot/	France
Finnish Robotics Association	www.psavolainen.net/robotics/index.html	Finland
HCC Robotica gg	members.tripod.com/~hccrobotica/	Netherlands
Mobil Robots Group	www.dai.ed.ac.uk/groups/mrg/MRG.html	Scotland
Pekee's Play Robotics Portal	www.pekee.fr/eng/low/ main.php?rub=Manif&cat=Team	France
Vancouver Island Robotics	www.vancouverislandrobotics.org/	Canada
Winnipeg Area Robotics Society	www.winnipegrobotics.com/	Canada
Yahoo Robotics Club	members.tripod.com/RoBoJRR/	Internet

Competitions:

AAAI Mobile Robot Competition	www.cs.cmu.edu/~aaairobot/	Sponsored by the American Association for Artificial Intelligence.
Aerial Robotics Competition	www.cs.cmu.edu/~aaairobot/	Helicopters and blimps go at it.
All Japan MicroMouse Contest	www.bekknet.ad.jp/~ntf/mouse/ mouse-e.html	Autonomous maze running competition in Japan.
All Japan Robot Sumo	www.fsi.co.jp/sumo-e	Robot sumo at its largest. 4000 robots entered in past years!
AMD Jerry Sanders Creative Design Contest	dc.cen.uiuc.edu/	University of Illinois contest open to all undergraduate and graduate students from any college or university.
Autonomous Robot Design Competition	web.mit.edu/6.270/	MIT's famous robot competition.
AUVS International Ground Robotic Competition	avdil.gtri.gatech.edu/AUVS/index.html	Autonomous ground vehicles navigate outdoor obstacle course. Competition boasts $20,000 in prize money and is open to college students only.
AUVSI's International Autonomous Underwater Vehicle Competition	www.auvsi.org/competitions	Underwater, (yes underwater), robotics competition. No water wings allowed.
BattleBots®	www.battlebots.com	Unbelievable bots, spectacular action, and terrific teams: What's not to love about this competition?!
BEAM	www.robotgames.com/	Fun competition with a minimalist approach to robotics.
Bot Bash	www.botbash.com/	Popular homegrown competition featuring various challenges and head-to-head combat.
BotBall	kipr.org/	High school students scramble to design, build and program a mobile robot in just six weeks! Sponsored by the KISS Institute for Practical Robotics (KIPR).

Canada First Robotic Games	www.canadafirst.org/	Canadian high school competition designed to motivate and "expand the pool of 'technology literate' students."
Carnegie Mellon Mobot Races	www.cs.cmu.edu/~mobot/	Carnegie Mellon competition for MObile roBOTs.
Central Jersey Robo Conflict	users.rcn.com/ljstier/rules.html	Remote controlled bots compete in a variety of games and beat each up.
Chicago BEST	www.chicagobest.org/	High school students team up with local businesses. Sponsored by BEST Robotics Inc. [The Boosting Engineering, Science and Technology] competition.
CIRC Autonomous Sumo Robot Competition	www.circ.mtco.com/01srules.htm	Regional competition where robots push each other around. Sponsored by the Central Illinois Robotics Club.
Critter Crunch	www.milehicon.org/critrule.htm	Object is to force opponents out of the arena or to literally crunch the competition. Features two weight classes: 2 and 20 pounders.
EuroBot	www.scenic-city.com/robot/	Annual autonomous robot competition in France. C'est super!
Federation of International Robot-soccer Associations	www.fira.net/	Get your kicks here. Association features various robot soccer competitions.
FIRST	www.usfirst.org/	Corporations sponsor local high school teams from across the US.
Intelligent Ground Vehicle Competition	www.secs.oakland.edu/ SECS_prof_orgs/PROF_AUVSI/index.html	Michigan completion held at Oakland University in Rochester.
Intelligent Robot Contest Festival	www.robotics.is.tohoku.ac.jp/inrof.html	Robot contest held in Sendai, Japan.
International Festival of Sciences and Technologies	www.robotik.org/defaultuk.htm	France's major robot competition. Includes walkers and soccers.
Lunar Robotic Construction Competition	www.technology.eku.edu/facstaff/ BOLES/SP2000/rules2000.htm	Build a badass lunar rover and win!
Manitoba Robot Games	www.scmb.mb.ca/pages/robotics.html	Large Canadian competition.
Micro Air Vehicle Competition	www.aero.ufl.edu/~issmo/mav/mav.htm	Design and build pint-size aerial vehicles and complete assigned mission. Competition held at the University of Florida.
North East Indiana Robot Games	www.geocities.com/CapeCanaveral/ Launchpad/8735/	Robot sumo competition in the heartland. Features three weight classes.
Northwest Robot Sumo Tournament	www.sinerobotics.com/sumo/	One of the biggest American sumo competitions.
OCAD Sumo Robot Challenge	www.student.ocad.on.ca/info/sumo/	Bashing/crashing/smashing robots. Sponsored by the Ontario College of Art & Design.
RoboCup	www.robocup.org/	The World Cup equivalent of international robot soccer competitions.
RoboFesta International Robot Games Festival	www.robofesta.net/e-contents/E_index.html	International robot games festival. Features a variety of competitions including a robot grand prix, RoboCup, and a design contest.
Robo-Pong 2000	www.tabletennisthesport.com/prod03.htm	Table tennis goes heavy metal.

RoboRama	www.dprg.org/dprg_contests.html	Sponsored by the Dallas Personal Robotics Group.
RoboRodentia	www.ieee.calpoly.edu/cs/RoboRodentia.html	Autonomous bots maneuver a maze in "The Quest for the Holy Cheese."
Robot Battles	www.scenic-city.com/robot/	Annual head-to-head robot combat competition held at Atlanta's Dragon*Con science fiction convention.
Robot Conflict	www.robotconflict.com/	Get your robot combat fix on the East Coast.
Robot Rally	www.botlanta.org/Rally/index.html	Robot combat in a vacuum! Fastest robot to vacuum 1/2 pound of rice wins. Sponsored by the Atlanta Hobby Robot Club and hosted by SciTrek.
Robot Rumble	www.robotrumble.co.uk	Small but growing UK competition inspired by BBC2's Robot Wars®. Gives fans ready to rumble a chance to see some of their favorite robots up close and personal.
Robot Rumbles	www.robotrumbles.com	Robots get down in dirty in Canada. Not happening yet, but we're hopeful.
Robot Sumo	www.robots.org/events.htm	Watch robots push each other around! Annual competition hosted by the SFRS and the San Francisco Exploratorium.
Robot Wars®	US: www.robotwars.com	
international:	www.robotmayhem.com	Ingenious bots, hyped fans, fire pits, dastardly house robots and bottomless pits: This competition has got it all.
Robothon	www.seattlerobotics.org/robothon/	Seattle Robotics Society annual competition.
Robotica®	tlc.discovery.com/fansites/robotica/robotica.html	Bots put to the ultimate challenges of speed, power, and strategy—all in a fast-paced, high-drama show. Not to be missed!
RSSC Robot Competition	www.dreamdroid.com/talentshow.htm	Sponsored by the Robotics Society of Southern California.
Singapore Robotic Games	guppy.mpe.nus.edu.sg/srg/srg	Eleven different competitions including legged robot race, wall climbing, and "robot battlefield."
The UC Davis Micromouse Competition	www.ece.ucdavis.edu/umouse/	Mini-robots negotiate their way through a variety of mazes.
Trinity College Fire Fighting Home Robot Contest	www.trincoll.edu/events/robot/	Autonomous robots put out fires in a maze.
Trinity LEGO Cybernetics Challenge	www.cs.tcd.ie/research_groups/cvrg/lego/index.html	Robot volleyball competition. Features bots built with Lego® Mindstorms™.
USA Robot Sumo	www.chibashoten.com/robot/	Japanese champions head to the US! $2000 first prize.
Walking Machine Challenge	www.sae.org/students/walking.htm	Society of Automotive Engineers SAE student competition.
Western Canadian Robot Games	www.robotgames.com/	Canada's premier robotic event includes sumo, BEAM, and hockey.

Bot Home Pages

Here are the home pages for those bots referenced in Robot Riots with live Web sites. Check 'em out!

Atomic Wedgie (Team Half Life)   www.getawedgie.com/

Backlash (Team Nightmare)   www.robotcombat.com

BioHazard (Team BioHazard)   www.robotbooks.com/biohazard.htm

Blade Runner (Team Carnivore)   www.teamcarnivore.com/creations/

Blendo (Team Blendo)   www.m5industries.com/blendo_main.html

Buddy Lee Stay in Your Seat (Team Fembot)   http://veritek.tripod.com/home.htm

Bulldog II (Team Bulldog)   www.bulldog-breed.co.uk

Chaos 2 (The Chaos Team)   www.gt-electronics.freeserve.co.uk/

Chiabot (Robot Action League)   www.execpc.com/~mwinter/robots/rt_chia.html

Chomp (Roger Korus)   http://mercury.spaceports.com/~korus/r-chomp.htm

Complete Control (Automatum Technologies)   www.automatum.com/

Deadblow (Team Deadblow)   www.deadblow.net.

Diesector (Team Mutant Robots)   www.mutantrobots.com/html/diesector.html

Díotóir (Team Díotóir)   www.esatclear.ie/~feoras/diotoir/

DooAll (Team I Wish I Knew)   www.robutz.com/

Dr. Inferno (The InfernoLab)   www.infernolab.com/

Diablo (Team Diablo)   http://home1.gte.net/res03xdq/index.htm

Endotherm (Team Saber)   www.teamsaber.com/endotherm.html

frenZy (Team Minus Zero)   www.tmz.com/

Fusion (Team Saber)   www.teamsaber.com/fusion.html

Hard Cheese (Team Hard Cheese)   http://liverdyne.50megs.com/about.html

Hazard (Team Delta/Team Hazard)   www.teamdelta.com/hazard/hazard-main.htm

Hypno-Disc (Team Hypno-Disc)   http://freespace.virgin.net/dave.rose/

JuggerBot (Team JuggerBot)   www.juggerbot.com

Killer B (Team Strange BRU)   www.mcmanis.com/chuck/robotics/killerB.html

La Machine (Team Vladiator)   http://home.earthlink.net/~gagecauchois/_wsn/page4.html

Little Sister (Team Big Brother)   www.teambigbro.co.uk/main.html

The Master (Team Sinister)   www.teamsinister.com/

Mauler 51-50 (The South Bay Robo Warriors)   www.mauler.net/

Mecha Tentoumushi (Robot Action League)   www.execpc.com/~mwinter/robots/rt_tento.html

Mechadon (Team Sinister)   www.teamsinister.com/

MechaVore (Team Shrapnel)   http://robertlawrencestudio.com/pages/mechavore/mechavore.html

Milly-Ann Bug (Rossums Raiders)   www.incarnate.co.uk/milly/team.html

Mini Inferno (The InfernoLab)   www.infernolab.com/

Minion (Team Coolrobots)   www.coolrobots.com/robots/minion.html

Mouser Mecha Catbot (Team Catbot)   www.merchantmanager.com/fonco/MM001.ASP?pageno=78

Nightmare (Team Nightmare)   www.robotcombat.com

Octobot (Bill Ruehl)   www.robotdude.com/

OverKill (Team Coolrobots)   www.coolrobots.com/robots/overkill.html

Pandora's Bot (Team Pandora)   http://sulacco.tripod.com/robot.htm

Pressure Drop (Automatum Technologies)   www.automatum.com/

Project X (Dion Brewington)   www.circ.mtco.com/99bot06.htm

Rammstein (Team Loki)   http://veritek.tripod.com/home.htm

Razer (Team Razer)	www.razer.co.uk/
Reactor (Team PNTA)	www.pnta.org/battlebots
Ronin (Team Ronin)	http://home.pacbell.net/roninsfx/
Run Amok (Team Run Amok)	www.open.org/~joerger/robotica.html?menu
Son of Whyachi (Team Whyachi)	www.teamwhyachi.com/
Squeegee (Sine Robotics)	www.sinerobotics.com/sumo/
S.L.A.M. (Team S.L.A.M.)	http://users.intercomm.com/stevenn/slamweb/Slam1.htm
The Snake (Team Sinister)	www.teamsinister.com/
Spike (Team Spike)	http://home.fiberia.com/root/nph-redirect.cgi?/lrobots
Sunshine Lollibot (Team Sunshine Lollibot)	www.olympus.net/personal/viviannk/webpics/index.html
T-Minus (Inertia Labs)	www.longnow.org/rhino/T-Minus01.htm
Tazbot (Team Mutant Robots)	www.mutantrobots.com/html/TAZBOT.html
Towering Inferno (The Infernolab)	www.infernolab.com/
Toro (Inertia Labs)	www.longnow.org/rhino/ToroSH.htm
Turbo (Team Loki)	http://veritek.tripod.com/home.htm
Vlad the Impaler (Team Vladiator)	www.loctite.com/new/pr_battlebots.html
Vladiator (Team Vladiator)	http://home.earthlink.net/~gagecauchois/_wsn/page4.html
Wedge of Doom (Team Hazard)	www.legalword.com/wod21.html
Ziggo (Team Ziggo)	www.jetstream.com/ziggo.html

Photo Credits

Thank you to the following who have kindly granted permission to use the photographs and images on the pages listed below:

BattleBots, Inc.®:
29, 33, 35, 37, 39, 40, 41, 44, 45, 46, 50, 55, 58, 61, 62, 63, 71, 80, 85, 90, 94, 105, 121, 123, 129, 133, 137, 144, 174

The Learning Channel, Inc.:
48, 124, 127, 131, 141, 161, 166, 187, 189, 191

Mentorn Barraclough Carey Ltd.:
5, 47, 53, 55, 59, 76, 140

Bettmann/Corbis:
9, 10, 12, 15, 19

Everett Collection:
7, 8, 11, 13, 14, 15, 16, 17, 18, 19

Jason Bardis/The Infernolab:
54, 96, 100, 144, 145

Michael Bastoni:
109, 116, 145, 184

The Burke family – 102, 111, 181

Bot Bash LLC – 84, 120

Computer Museum of Boston and Dr. Joanne Pransky – 102

April and Fon Davis – 83, 93, 164

Nola Garcia and Starbot:
26, 52, 118, 168, 184

Grant Imahara – 73, 91, 149, 172

Industrial Light & Magic – 24, 153

Roger Korus – 81

LEGO® – 23

Jonathan Ridder – 47, 75

Jim Smentowski – 42, 155

Tony Somerfield – 139

Team Carnivore – 99, 135, 162

Team Díotoír:
21, 49, 69, 92, 170, 180, 153

Team Raptor – 113

Team Razer:
22, 43, 79, 88, 175, 190

Team Robot Widows:
25, 107, 142

Marc Thorpe – 31

Rik Winter – 146, 147

The Winter family – 67, 78, 157

Will and Cassidy Wright – 86